RUPERT

1950 ANNUAL

Certificate

This certificate offers a guarantee from Express Newspapers and Pedigree Books that the Rupert Annual is a close reproduction of the original publication that first appeared in 1950.

Each attractively presented copy is a limited edition and bears its own individual number, making it a unique collectors' item. It is certain to provide timeless quality entertainment to the reader today, just as it did all those decades ago.

Rupert Editor

Book Number: 06386

06386

4/-

RUPERT'S TOY RAILWAY PUZZLE

"I say, you chaps," says Rupert, "let's have a go at this problem that my Uncle Bruno has given us. Look! he's set out my toy railway in three lines all joining, and he's put two little trucks and an engine on them. Up here, near the card marked 'A', is a tiny siding that will just hold one truck, but the engine can't get into it. He wants us to do some shunting with the engine and see if we can make the trucks change places."

Can you do it? You may change the points so that all the lines are in use, but the trucks must not move unless the engine is pulling or pushing them and none of them must be lifted from the rails. And remember that the engine cannot get into the siding at "A".

ADVENTURES of RUPERT

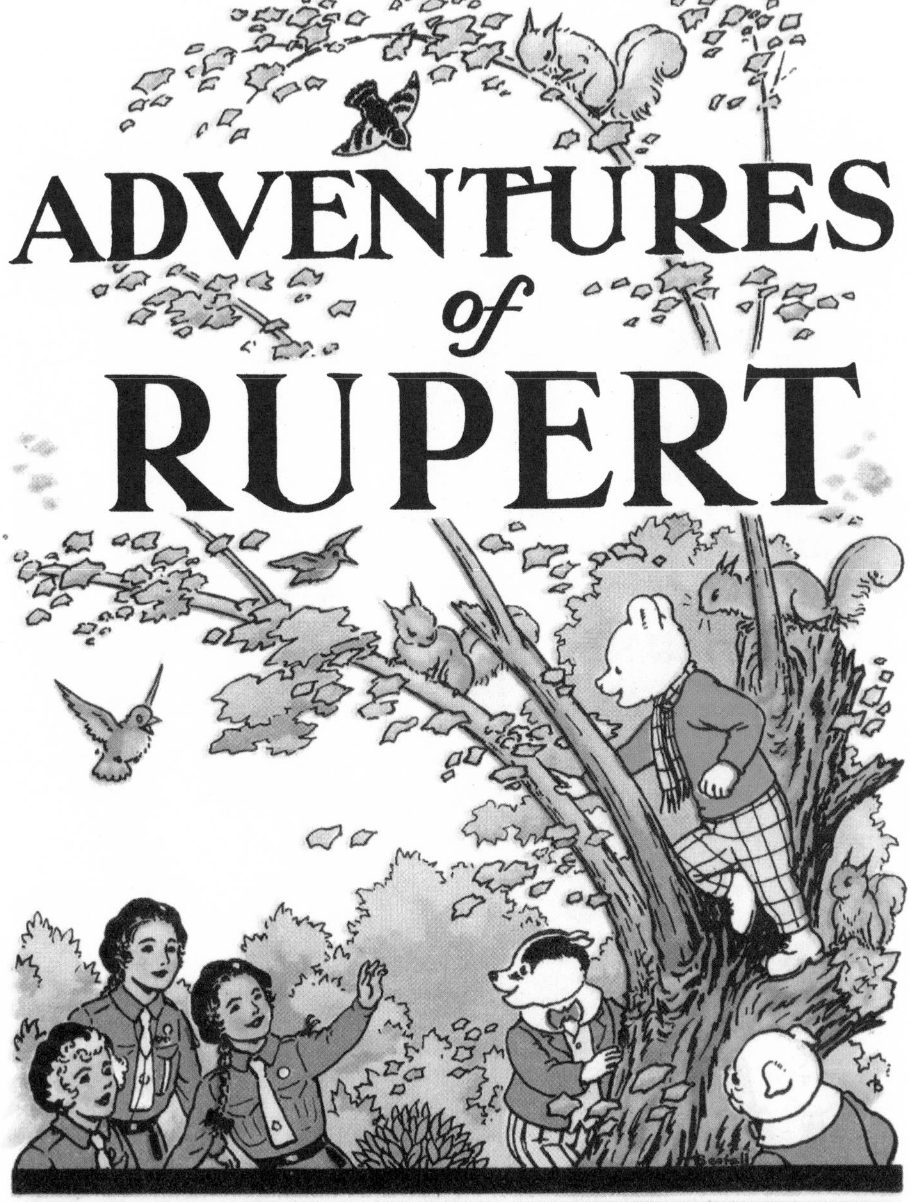

A **DAILY EXPRESS** PUBLICATION

CONTENTS

RUPERT'S SILVER TRUMPET

Telling how Rupert received the wrong present and summoned the Palace guard by mistake

RUPERT ASKS ALGY FOR ADVICE

Near Christmas, Rupert sighs, "Oh dear;
What present shall I choose this year."

He thinks he'll take a walk outside,
Then finds that Algy can't decide.

His friends try hard to help the bear,
But soon hear music in the air.

"Look, Rupert, it's the village band!"
The little chums all think it's grand.

"You look worried, Rupert," says Mr. Bear one morning. "What's the matter?" Rupert sighs, "I'm writing to Santa Claus to ask for my Christmas presents and I don't know what I want," he says. "I think I'll go for a walk and make up my mind." Rupert strolls slowly along, trying to think, when he almost bumps into his pal Algy Pug. "I say, can you help me?" says the little bear. "I don't know what to ask Santa Claus for." "How extraordinary," laughs Algy. "I'm in the same boat."

When Willie hears Rupert's problem he tries to look very wise. "It's difficult, isn't it?" he murmurs. "I know one thing you could do. . . ." He is suddenly interrupted by a shout from Algy. "Hush," calls the little pug. "Listen a minute." Rupert and Willie listen carefully and, sure enough, faint sounds come from across the common. In a moment they are scampering towards the sound until they meet a brass band marching through the cutting. "Ooh soldiers!" shouts Willie.

RUPERT IS SHOWN THE AIRPLANE

"I know," cries Rupert, "what to do.
We'll ask for drum and trumpets too."

To have a band would be great fun,
So home to write their notes they run.

A cat calls Rupert back again,
To see a lovely model 'plane.

Says Rupert Bear, "It's strange to me!
There's no one here that I can see."

"I say, why can't we have a band of our own?" cries Rupert. "That would solve all our problems. Algy and I could ask for trumpets and you, Willie, might ask for a drum." Algy and Willie think that Rupert's idea is splendid. So off they run to write their letters to Santa Claus, but before he has gone far a funny little noise makes Rupert turn. "Why it's Dinkie!" he cries. "Why are you so far from home?" But Dinkie won't answer and seems to want Rupert to turn back again.

Dinkie acts so curiously that Rupert turns and finds himself being led back to a part of the common. As he peeps over a grassy ridge he sees a lovely model airplane there. "My, what a beauty!" he gasps. "I've never seen such a lovely model." Rupert looks carefully over the 'plane but he doesn't dare to try to start it. "It's a great mystery," he murmurs. "Why should the owner have left such a lovely thing unguarded? Well, we'd better go home, but I'll certainly come and see it again."

RUPERT, AND PALS POST LETTERS

At home once more, he tells his Mum,
About the trumpets and the drum.

The chums run down to catch the post,
There's no doubt now what they want most.

Now Dinkie turns to stand and stare,
He's seen somebody hiding there.

A Golly! He has a big sack
Of children's letters on his back.

Rupert puzzles over the mystery of the little airplane as he runs home, but he can make nothing of it. Indoors he tells his mother how he solved the problem that had worried him earlier on. "I've decided to ask Santa Claus for a trumpet," he says, as he starts to write. When his letter is finished Rupert seals it carefully and runs to the pillar-box to post it just as Algy and Willie come hurrying up. Just then Dinkie the cat strolls up and stares intently into the hedge.

The three pals talk excitedly for a while then Willie and Algy go home, but as Rupert is walking away a noise makes him turn. Dinkie is now staring at the pillar-box. "What's the matter with that cat now?" he murmurs. "Good gracious, there's someone hiding." Hurrying to see who it is Rupert finds a large Golly staring at him, and the door of the pillar-box is open. "Here, how did you open that?" cries the little bear. "I have a key to every pillar-box," says Golly calmly.

RUPERT RECEIVES A PARCEL

"I come from Santa Claus," he cries,
To Rupert's very great surprise.

"Now," Golly says, "I'll have to go;
This model 'plane is mine, you know."

High up into the sky he soars,
To take the sack to Santa Claus.

Next morning, Rupert cries, "Look there!
A box addressed to Rupert Bear."

Seeing that Rupert is worried at finding the pillar-box open the Golly explains. "My job is to sort the mail before the postman comes," he says. "I pick out all the letters adressed to Santa Claus and take them straight up to him." The Golly leads Rupert away at a brisk trot with Dinkie, who is determined not to be left behind, following. Straight up the small ridge they go and Golly drops his sack into the model airplane. "Is that yours?" gasps the little bear. "Of course it is," laughs Golly.

The model 'plane soars away almost silently just as Algy and Willie come running up. "That was Santa Claus's Golly and he's taking all our letters straight to him," explains Rupert. He tells them all about the queer meeting before rushing home to tell Mr. and Mrs. Bear of the odd things that have happened. Next morning he goes shopping with his father and on their return they stop suddenly, for a parcel is lying on the step. "It's addressed to you, Rupert," says Mrs. Bear.

RUPERT GETS A WARNING

A trumpet! Rupert jumps with joy,
Oh, what a really splendid toy.

It will not play when Rupert blows,
So off to find his friends he goes.

Poor Algy nearly hurts his throat,
And then he blows a long, clear note.

A lot of birds come flying round,
They want to know who made that sound.

Rupert unfastens his parcel with trembling fingers and in great excitement he lifts a new, shining trumpet out of the box. Rupert blows gently and then harder but the trumpet makes no sound at all. Then the others blow and have no better result. "How queer. There must be some trick," says Rupert, and runs out to ask his pals what they think. Almost at once he meets Algy and Willie looking rather glum. "My trumpet's here," says Rupert. "It's a beauty, but I have no idea how to play it."

"Here, let me have a go," says Algy. "I was once shown how to blow a trumpet by a Boy Scout." Just when he is getting red in the face, a long, clear note rings out. Rupert has just taken the silver trumpet when a bird arrives and flaps wildly around his head. "Hi, where did you get that?" he cries. "It's Rupert's Christmas present," says Algy. "We can't disturb anyone by playing it up here," adds Willie. "Oh, can't you," screams the bird, getting excited. "Just you wait and see."

RUPERT MEETS THE ARMY

Now Willie points into the air,
"Just look at all those soldiers there!"

The timid mouse soon runs away,
But both his chums decide to stay.

Straight up to them the soldiers go,
"Where's Santa Claus?" they want to know.

"We are his guards," the leader cries,
"This trumpet called us from the skies."

The bird's warning makes Rupert feel nervous and suddenly a cry from Willie makes him turn. "Quick!" shouts the little mouse. "Up in the sky! Can you see them? A lot of tiny men walking down on the sunbeams!" The first of the figures comes to earth and the next minute all the strangers are marching towards them. The corporal halts. "Where is Santa Claus?" he asks. "Is he in danger?" Rupert stares. "I don't know. Why should he be? I don't understand what you mean."

"We are the guards of the Winter Castle, the home of Santa Claus," he says. "We were summoned here by the sound of the trumpet." He frowns darkly. "Explain this, little bear, or there will be trouble for you." "Please, I wrote to Santa Claus for a trumpet," Rupert says. "Golly took my letter and this arrived on my doorstep to-day." The corporal takes the trumpet. "There has been a bad mistake," he growls; "this is only blown when there is danger to Santa Claus."

GOLLY FLIES BACK TO EARTH

There's some mistake, that is quite plain,
And so his men go back again.

"That's good," the soldier says, "and now
That trumpet must go back, somehow."

"I'll leave you to explain," he cries,
As Golly's 'plane towards them flies.

When Golly lands, they run along,
To ask him if the trumpet's wrong.

The corporal thinks for a minute. "The worst part of this mistake is that it has left Santa Claus without guards," he says. Turning, he gives a couple of orders and all the toy soldiers turn to the left and to the amazement of Rupert and Algy they march off the ridge and disappear up a sunbeam. The tiny corporal frowns. "I must get that trumpet back to Winter Castle," he says, and taking a whistle from his pocket he blows a note that is so thin and high that Rupert can hardly hear it.

Putting the whistle back in his pocket the little corporal turns to Rupert. "I have believed your story, little bear," he says. "I must go." And without any effort he turns and marches away into the air. Rupert then notices a small speck in the sky which is gradually getting bigger. "Look, it's Golly's 'plane," cries Algy. The model 'plane lands near the two friends and the pilot clambers out. Rupert races towards him. "Have a look at this," cries the little bear. "Is it really mine?"

RUPERT RUNS FOR WILLIE

"Well," Golly cries, "that's very queer,
I've made a bad mistake, I fear."

The poor Golly is most upset,
It's quite the worst thing he's done yet.

He says, "I'll take the trumpet too,
And bring another one for you."

Now Rupert thinks of Willie Mouse,
So off they hurry to his house.

The Golly seizes the trumpet and stares at it. "How on earth did you get this?" he asks, "and did you really manage to blow it? This is Santa Claus's trumpet and is only used to call the guard of toy soldiers together in time of danger." The two friends run to the village with the Golly and fetch the brown paper and box out of Rupert's cottage. Golly looks carefully at the address. "There's no doubt of it," he says. "That's my writing. This is the worst mistake I have ever made."

The Golly hurries back to his model 'plane and puts the silver trumpet into it. "Don't worry, little bear," he says; "you shall have your present. Come back here in an hour's time and see what I send you." And next moment he whizzes away into the sky. Having an hour to wait Rupert thinks of Willie the mouse. "What a pity he ran away when those toy soldiers came," he says. "Let's fetch him." So he and Algy race to Willie's cottage to tell their little pal all that has happened.

RUPERT UNPACKS THE PARCEL

Together now, they wait to see,
What Rupert's present now will be.

The parcel drops towards the ground,
And lands quite gently, safe and sound.

"My word!" says Rupert in surprise,
"A trumpet cannot be that size."

But when the box is opened wide,
They find more instruments inside.

Willie the mouse is thrilled with Rupert's story and he runs with his pals back to the common. "Look, there's the model 'plane," shouts Rupert. It flies round and round and then starts to climb again. Rupert gets very worried. Then to his delight a parachute opens out and floats gently down. "What a topping idea," cries Algy. "Now it can't come to any harm." "The wind's carrying it away," says Rupert; "come on, let's see where it lands." And all three set off in pursuit.

They scamper across the common and they laugh when they see that Dinkie has turned up again. "Well you are an inquisitive creature," says Rupert. In great excitement the three pals take off the parachute and unpack the parcel. Willie gives a shout, "Look, here is a fine big drum. But that is what I asked for. You don't want a drum, do you, Rupert?" But Rupert is gazing at the silver trumpet in his hand. "Look in the box. There are lots of other things there," says Algy.

RUPERT FORMS HIS BAND

The chums exclaim with great delight,
For now they have their band all right.

Bill Badger and the rabbits run,
To see if they can join the fun.

The people stare as on they come,
With Willie banging on his drum.

"Well," Rupert sighs, "I must confess,
Our band to-day was no success."

The little friends can hardly wait to try out the things in the box. Willie bangs happily on the drum while Rupert and Algy blow loudly, and Rupert's friends come running from all directions to see who is making all the music. "I say, what is going on up here?" says Bill Badger, as he runs up to the little group. "You'd never guess," says Rupert. "Santa Claus sent me a whole boxful of things to play so that we can all have one!" So the little pals quickly choose what they will play.

They get in line and, leaving the box and parachute to be picked up later, they march sturdily into Nutwood all playing as loudly as they can and trying to keep in step to Willie's drum-beats. Mr. Bear stares in astonishment at the things that Rupert shows him. "We're going to have a band of our own," says the little bear. "We've had one march but it didn't sound quite like a real band." "Well, why not all try playing the same tune," says Mr. Bear. "That's a good idea," says Rupert.

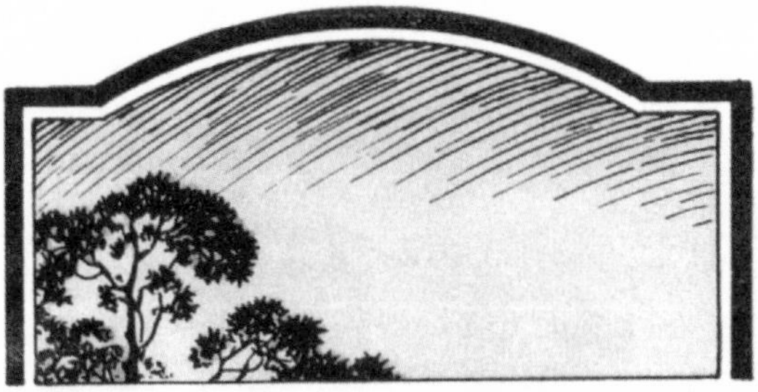

RUPERT and MARGOT'S HOUSE

How Rupert with the help of his pals rescues Margot from the Giant's Castle

RUPERT OFFERS HIS HELP

Now Rupert's pleased to hear one day,
That Margot has come back to stay.

So out he goes at once to see,
If Margot will come back to tea.

Her Grannie says that she may go,
But where she is she does not know.

As Rupert searches all around,
He finds her hanky on the ground.

When Mrs. Bear returns from shopping she asks Rupert, "Did you know that your friend Margot has come back to Nutwood?" "Margot, I'd nearly forgotten her," cries Rupert. "Please may I go and ask her to tea?" Having got permission, Rupert runs to the edge of the village where he meets Margot's granny and he gives his message. "That's very kind of you," says the old lady. "I should love Margot to come but I am worried about her these days." "What's the matter?" asks Rupert. "Can I help?"

"It's such a long time since Margot was here that she is afraid that everybody has forgotten her," she says. "Every morning she goes out alone until evening and will never tell me where she has been." "She needn't be afraid of me," says Rupert; "I'll go and search for her at once." Soon after he reaches the trees he picks up a small handkerchief. "It's got the name of Margot on it," he murmurs. "What have you found, Rupert?" calls a cheery voice, then the Rabbit twins run to join him.

RUPERT FINDS A NOTICE

The rabbits join him, then they hear
A hedgehog calling them quite near.

He tells them Margot is close by,
So off they go once more to try.

"Just look at that!" cries Rupert Bear,
"A brand new notice board up there."

The rabbits run into the wood,
Though Rupert calls them, it's no good.

Rupert shows Margot's handkerchief to the twins and tells them why he is searching for her. "You'll know her when you see her," says Rupert. "She is a shy, old-fashioned little girl." "And I can tell you where she is," pipes a little voice, as Horace the hedgehog peeps out of a bush. "She's in a dangerous part of the wood." The three little pals run along the footpath until the wood becomes thicker. Then Rupert pauses. "There's a sign-board here," he says, "let's look at it."

Rupert and the twins are puzzled by the strange sign. "I was along this path the other week and the sign-board wasn't here then," says Rupert. "It must be new." Rupert wants to go another way but Reggie gazes at the little side-path leading behind the sign-board. "I can't understand it at all," he says. "That board wasn't there last week. I'm going to try and find out why it was put there." "Jolly good idea," says Rex. And before Rupert can stop them they run down the private path and disappear.

RUPERT FINDS MARGOT

When Rupert thinks he'll go as well,
Which path to take he cannot tell.

A little farther, Rupert sees
Another notice on the trees.

Then, all at once, he has a shock,
For there is Margot by a rock.

The little girl greets Rupert Bear,
Then tells him what she's doing there.

"Those twins are a nuisance," murmurs Rupert. "The new sign-board was put up there to keep people out and now they have gone in." Then another thought strikes him. "Margot may be in that part of the wood," he says. "Perhaps I had better follow after all." Not knowing which way the little rabbits have gone Rupert chooses the right-hand fork of the little path, and soon he spies something. "Why it's another sign," he murmurs; "and I do believe it is spelt wrongly, too."

Creeping round the rocks he comes face to face with a little girl. "Why it's Margot!" he cries. "Don't you remember me?" "Of course I remember you, Rupert," she smiles. "How did you find me?" Rupert shows Margot the handkerchief he picked up. "I wanted you to come to tea," he says. "But why are you in this private part of the wood?" "It isn't really private," says Margot. "It's part of a lovely game I'm playing." "So that's why the signs are all spelt wrongly," laughs Rupert.

RUPERT SEES THE HOUSE

She found a little house one day,
And now she loves to come and play.

"What's that?" cries Rupert with a frown,
As earth and stones come tumbling down.

"It's nothing," Margot tells her chum,
"Look, there's my lovely house. Do come!"

The little bear with wonder cries,
"Why, everything is just our size."

Margot explains the game. "I came here to look for flowers," she says, "and I found a little house. It doesn't belong to anyone so I am living in it and I'm putting up these notices to keep people out." Rupert remembers the words of Horace the hedgehog. "This part of the wood is supposed to be very dangerous," he says. Margot stares at him strangely. "I haven't seen any danger except for the earthquakes," she says. Just then the earth trembles and lumps of earth and pebbles tumble from above.

When the shaking stops Rupert wants to take Margot away from the wood but she insists on showing him what she has found. "Those earthquakes don't seem to hurt anybody," she says, "and look, there is my secret. Isn't it lovely?" In front of him, under the shelter of the overhanging cliff, Rupert sees a tiny house painted in bright colours and quite new. The two pals run into the little house where Rupert gazes around in wonder. "If it wasn't so big it might be a doll's house," he says.

RUPERT RUNS TO SHELTER

He runs outside to look around,
Then calls, "Just see what I have found."

But now the shaking starts once more,
And this is much worse than before.

"Come on!" cries Margot, "let us hide."
But Rupert wants to be outside.

He climbs inside a hollow tree,
Then wonders where his chum can be.

Rupert goes outside and stares carefully all round. "I say," he cries, "the back of this house is quite plain. There's no paint on it at all, and look there *is* a big catch up there. If you move that the whole wall will come away." They go into the little house again and Margot peers into a cupboard. "It's no good," she sighs. "There's nothing to show whom the place belongs to." Before Rupert can reply there is a clatter, and he glances sharply out of the window as the house starts to shake and wobble.

The shaking of the hillside gets more violent. Margot dodges into a cupboard but Rupert is very worried. Calling to Margot to follow he dashes out to find shelter while bits of the cliff fall around him. He finds, as he leaves the rocks behind, the earth does not tremble so much, but he pops into a hollow tree for safety and waits for Margot. "She must have stayed in the cupboard," he thinks. "I do hope that overhanging cliff has not fallen on the little house. I must go back and see."

RUPERT SEES THE GIANT

So Rupert hurries to the place,
But of the house there is no trace.

A lizard, who is sitting there,
Says he can help the little bear.

A giant built that house one day,
And now he's taken it away.

Poor Margot is inside it still,
So Rupert watches from a hill.

Rupert hurries up the hill. As he reaches the overhanging cliff he stops and stares with amazement. The little house has vanished. "Margot! Margot!" he shouts. Getting no answer Rupert walks towards the cliffs and sees a large lizard sitting on a rock. "I say," he cries, "do you know what has happened to the little house that was here, just like a giant doll's house?" "That's exactly what it was," says the lizard. "The giant made it and left it in the shelter of the cliff to dry. Now he's taken it away."

Rupert is horrified at what he has heard. "Did you say giant?" he cries. "How awful! Where has the giant gone?" The lizard, seeing that Rupert is unhappy, leads the way across the rocks. Looking across country they see a dark castle looming against the sky and striding towards it is the figure of the giant. He is carrying the doll's house by the chimney. "You needn't worry too much," says the lizard, "the giant made that house as a surprise for his daughter, so he's sure to take care of it."

RUPERT TAKES ADVICE

He hurries back to Nutwood now,
For he must rescue her somehow.

The lizard says, "You must not mind;
That giant really is quite kind."

And then he says, "The way to go
Is by the river bank, you know."

The rabbits have a sailing boat,
Which they can quickly get afloat.

In spite of the lizard's words Rupert does worry very much. Galloping through the woods he finds Reggie and Rex and pours out the whole story. The twins stare at him. "So that's why Horace the hedgehog said that part of the wood was dangerous," gasps Reggie. Rupert doesn't notice the lizard has followed until he appears on a boulder. "I told you not to worry," says the creature. "Even if the giant did see your little friend he won't hurt her. He's a kind old thing."

"You'd certainly find it hard to follow that giant across that rough country," says the lizard; "but the river at the bottom of the hill comes from that direction. Take my advice, if you want to enter that dark castle wear your Wellingtons!" Feeling much happier the little pals race back to Nutwood. "I wonder why the lizard told me to wear my Wellingtons," says Rupert. "We haven't any Wellingtons," says Rex; "but we have a sailing-boat. Come on, Reggie. Let's go and get it ready."

Rupert and Margot's House

RUPERT SETS SAIL

So Rupert hurries home to say,
Where he is going for the day.

Down to the river runs the bear,
And finds the twins already there.

Now, full of hope, the three set sail,
To help their friend, they must not fail.

At last the castle comes in sight,
And Rupert gets ashore all right.

Rupert runs to get his Wellingtons and his story comes tumbling out breathlessly. "I've found Margot," he cries. "The twins have a boat and we're going to sail after her and we may be a long time." "Goodness," smiles Mrs. Bear, "I'd better get you some food for four people, hadn't I?" After thanking Mrs. Bear for the sandwiches, Rupert runs to the river where he has arranged to meet the twins and he finds his pals are there. "We've only just got the boat here," shouts Rex.

The three pals leave Nutwood behind as the river winds between the hills, and then the banks become rocky and at last the dark towers of the great castle appear ahead of them, soaring up into the sky. "I do believe the river is going to take us right up to the castle walls," says Rupert. At length Rex steers the boat to the shore just where some broken rocks come down to the river. "You two had better stay and look after the boat while I see how we can get into the castle," says Rupert.

RUPERT USES HIS WELLINGTONS

He climbs up to the castle wall,
But finds no entrance there at all.

And now, a waterfall quite near,
Makes Rupert think there's something queer.

A tunnel through the castle goes,
And it's from this the water flows.

"I've got my boots," thinks Rupert Bear,
"There's room for me to walk through there."

Rupert struggles up the sides of the broken rocks on which the castle is built until he reaches a point where he can look around. "I can't see a way in at all this side," he murmurs. "One thing I cannot understand. Why did the lizard tell me to wear my Wellingtons?" Hearing the splash of a waterfall he follows the sound and is soon drinking gratefully. When he is refreshed he glances up to the top of the waterfall. "There's something odd about this," he murmurs.

Being very inquisitive he climbs up the castle walls and finds them too steep and slippery, so he turns and clambers the long way round and reaches the stream again above the fall. "Now I understand what the lizard meant." What has made Rupert so excited is that the little stream is flowing in a tunnel right through the castle walls. As he bends down and peers through he can see daylight at the other end. "Of course," he chuckles, "this is why the lizard told me to wear my Wellingtons!"

RUPERT MEETS MR. FROG

He paddles through the stream somehow,
Then finds he's in the castle now.

A frog is standing by a pail,
So Rupert tells him his strange tale.

This kindly frog says he will show,
The little bear just where to go.

Now Rupert sees upon the floor,
The little house he saw before.

Rupert finds that the water is flowing out of a round pond set in a stone courtyard. "This is queer," he whispers. Creeping on, Rupert reaches an enormous bucket and finds that he is being stared at by a very big frog. "Who on earth are you?" says the frog. "Oh, please," says Rupert, "I'm looking for a little girl. She hid in a very large doll's house and a giant walked off with her." The frog blinks solemnly. "That's a strange tale," he says. "I've seen a doll's house here, but I've seen no little girl."

Rupert begs the frog to tell him where the doll's house is, and then the creature blinks at him again. "You're lucky to be able to see the doll's house at all," he says; "the giant may come to take it away at any moment." When he has led Rupert to the doorway the frog hops away again, while the little bear pauses and listens. Then he goes inside and looks at the doll's house from behind the leg of one of the giant's chairs. "I'm in luck," he breathes; "there seems to be no one about."

RUPERT GETS A SHOCK

He looks inside the house with care,
But finds that Margot isn't there.

"Where can she be?" he sighs. "Oh dear!"
And then he hears her voice quite near.

They are so pleased to meet again,
Then footsteps they can hear quite plain.

The chums are scared they will be found,
And so they hide without a sound.

Rupert reaches the doll's house and makes straight for the cupboard. "Margot is not there," he gasps. "I wonder if she ran out of the house when I was in the hollow tree." Wondering whether his exciting journey has been all in vain, Rupert comes out of the doll's house and a loud whisper makes him spin round. Peering at him from behind a huge piece of furniture is Margot. "Oh, Rupert," she cries, "are you here, too? Where are we?" "Hush, not so loud," whispers Rupert; "I'll tell you what happened."

"Those earthquakes were really the giant walking about," he explains. Suddenly he stops and clutches her arms. "Can you hear something?" he whispers. "I believe someone is coming. We must hide." At one side of the great room is a curtain and they make a dash for it just in time. No sooner are they behind it than the giant enters, strides across to the doll's house and picks it up again by the chimney, and goes out, passing so close to the pals that they hardly dare breathe.

RUPERT FOLLOWS MR. FROG

But luckily the giant goes by,
"We're saved!" breathes Rupert with a sigh.

Just then the frog comes back to say,
That he can help them get away.

The frog explains, "Just follow me,
And very soon you shall be free."

He takes them to a great, strong door,
But there's a hole just by the floor.

When the giant has disappeared Rupert breathes more freely. "Whew, that was a near go," he murmurs. "I'm glad he didn't see us." Creeping out to a corner in the wall they peep out, but the giant has disappeared. Just then the great frog comes lolloping along the flagstones. "Hallo, I've found my friend Margot," says Rupert, "but I can't think how to get her home. If we told the giant that we were here do you think he would take us. A lizard told us that the giant is a kind person."

"It might be risky," says the frog. "Follow me carefully, for I have a better idea." Obediently, Rupert takes Margot's hand and follows. At the end of the wall the little party reach an enormous door fastened by great iron bars and hinges. "There you are," says the frog. "That hole at the bottom was made by mice and if they can get through it you should be able to. So good-bye and good luck! You'll find the little bridge outside."

RUPERT REJOINS THE TWINS

The chums squeeze through the hole with ease,
Then run to shelter 'neath the trees.

"Who's that?" exclaims the little bear,
"I think I heard somebody there."

It's Reggie Rabbit, who has come
To see what's happened to his chum.

Poor Rex and Reggie turn quite pale,
When Rupert tells his thrilling tale.

Rupert and Margot squeeze through the hole in the door. Sure enough they find a bridge outside and hurry over it. Once he is back among the trees Rupert feels safer. "I haven't much idea where we are," he says; "I expect Rex and Reggie are tired of waiting for us in their boat." Finding a good view-point he spies the river not far away. "I believe we can reach it this way," he declares. All at once he pauses. "I can hear something moving down below," he breathes.

Rupert edges forward as the sound comes nearer and next moment the anxious face of Reggie appears. "Oh, Rupert," cries the little Rabbit, "you've been away so long. We thought you must be in trouble. Have you found any way we can look for Margot?" As he speaks Margot herself comes and smiles over Rupert's shoulder. "You needn't look any further," she laughs. When Reggie has got over his surprise he helps Margot down the slope where Rex is waiting with the boat.

RUPERT RETURNS WITH MARGOT

The wind's against them now, and so
To get to Nutwood they must row.

All Rupert's chums are waiting now,
For they have heard the news somehow.

When Margot's Granny comes their way,
She's pleased to find her look so gay.

Next day, when Margot comes to tea,
She settles down quite happily.

For the journey back to Nutwood the little friends find that the wind is against them, but the stream is flowing in their direction so the twins get out the oars and row steadily while Rupert steers and Margot eats most of the sandwiches. In Nutwood there is some excitement. Bill Badger and Podgy and Pong-Ping and Algy and Willie are the first to reach the river bank. "Here we are, back again," says Rupert; "and, look, there is quite a crowd to meet us."

Margot's Granny is worrying about the little girl when the sound of happy voices reaches her ears. "Oh, Rupert," cries Granny, "however did you manage it?" "Just you wait and see," laughs Rupert. "Margot will tell you the whole story herself." Next day Margot comes to tea with Rupert while Mrs. Bear listens to the exciting story. "I'm coming to school with you soon," says Margot. "It's time I learnt to spell, isn't it? Then if I write any more signs I shall do them properly."

RUPERT and the JUMPING FISH

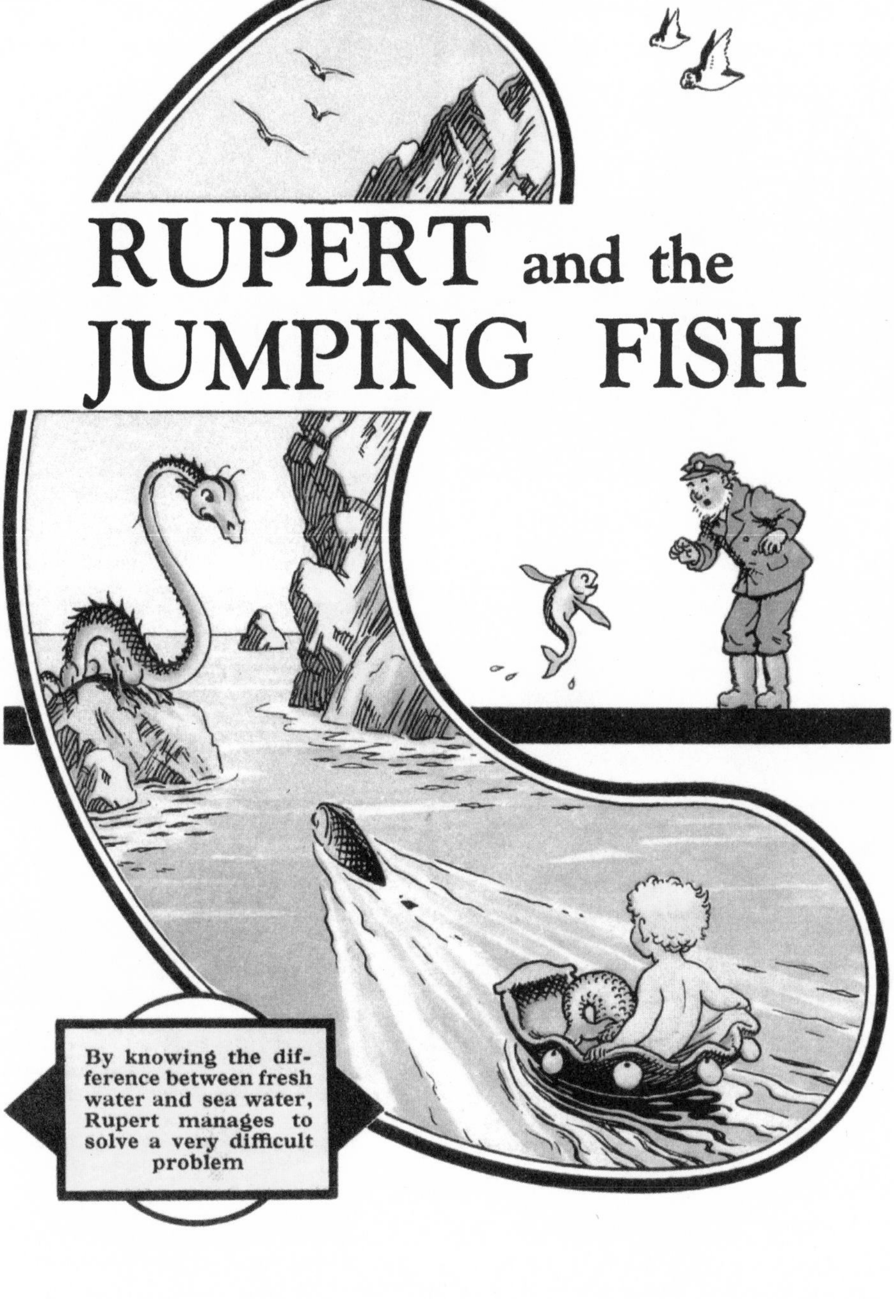

By knowing the difference between fresh water and sea water, Rupert manages to solve a very difficult problem

RUPERT HEARS THE NEWS

Says Mr. Bear, "The day is fine,
Why don't you make a fishing line?"

Now Rupert thinks this would be fun,
And very soon his rod is done.

The country mouse tells Rupert Bear,
"I saw a jumping fish in there."

They sit and wait, until at last,
This strange new fish goes swimming past.

Running into the garden Rupert finds his father busily cutting away long shoots from the base of an old tree. "Can I help you, Daddy?" he asks "No, thank you," smiles Mr. Bear, "but if you like you can take one of those shoots and a bent pin and then go fishing." "Oo, that's a jolly good idea!" cries Rupert. "I'll start now." He runs off and on the way he glances upwards. "What's the matter with all those birds to-day," he thinks. "There must be something queer down there."

Rupert goes off at top speed and arrives at the river bank to find 'Rastus, the country mouse. "I say, 'Rastus," says Rupert breathlessly, "what's the matter with all these birds?" "There's a new kind of fish here," says 'Rastus. "It has come up from the sea and it keeps jumping out of the water." The little pals lie on the bank and gaze patiently into the water. Then 'Rastus stiffens. "Look, just under the surface," he whispers. They wait silently. "Why doesn't he jump?" whispers Rupert.

Rupert and the Jumping Fish

RUPERT GETS A MESSAGE

A little bird calls, "Rupert, stay!
That fish was calling you to-day."

Now Rupert thinks, "My rod I'll hide";
And soon the fish is by his side.

He says, "Your friend needs help from you,
And I will tell you what to do."

He stays no longer to explain,
But plunges in the stream again.

At length 'Rastus says that he must go home and wanders off. Suddenly a bird flaps its wings at the little bear. "Hi, young Rupert," he squawks, "have you seen that queer fish? Each time he jumped he called your name." Greatly puzzled, Rupert returns thoughtfully to the river. "Why, of course," he says, "he was frightened because I was carrying a fishing-rod." Hiding the rod, he sits and watches. Soon a fish leaps from the water. "Oh, please, are you Rupert Bear?" asks a tiny voice.

"Thank goodness I've found you," says a little gasping voice. "The sea-serpent is in some sort of trouble and he wants you to help him. Meet me at Rocky Bay and I'll take you to him," says the little fish, panting. Just then the diving-board shakes and 'Rastus joins Rupert. "I heard voices and came back," he says. Rupert sighs. "It's all very mysterious," he says. "The fish says the sea-serpent wants me to help him." 'Rastus gives a snort. "How could you help a sea-serpent?" he asks.

RUPERT TELLS HIS MOTHER

"Well," Rupert says, "that puzzles me;
But I should like to go and see."

So Rupert hurries home to know
If he, to Rocky Bay, may go.

"There's Sailor Sam!" cries Rupert Bear,
"I'll ask him how to get down there."

Sam's friend, the Captain, knows the way,
Because he lives at Rocky Bay.

Still feeling puzzled and very excited, Rupert goes to pick up his fishing-rod. Leaving 'Rastus, Rupert hurries home and throws open the door. "I say, Mummy," he calls, "there's been a jumping fish in the river; he says that the sea-serpent wants me to help him out of some trouble. May I go to him?" Mrs. Bear looks startled. Then her face clears as she thinks that Rupert is playing some kind of let's-pretend game. "All right, run along," she smiles, "and mind you don't bring him home to tea."

Getting his mother's permission, Rupert runs off happily. After hurrying through the wood Rupert comes to a shack and soon he is telling Sailor Sam what has happened and how anxious he is to get to Rocky Bay. The sailor stares. "Well, young Rupert," he says, "you do get some of the craziest ideas I've ever heard of, but your luck is in this time. This is my old skipper, Cap'n Binnacle, who has called to see me. He lives at Rocky Bay, so if you ask him nicely he will take you there."

RUPERT GOES TO ROCKY BAY

He says, "It isn't very far;
I'll take you with me in my car."

The car is old, but goes all right,
And soon the bay comes into sight.

The Captain says, "I leave you here.
I hope your fish will soon appear."

A fish comes swimming to the shore,
Much larger than the one before.

Cap'n Binnacle takes Rupert behind the shack and there stands one of the oldest cars Rupert has ever seen. Saying good-bye to Sailor Sam, Rupert and Cap'n Binnacle enter the ancient motor-car, and they are soon rattling along the road. "This is jolly," laughs Rupert. "I've never been in such a noisy car. If that jumping fish is in the bay he will hear us coming!" Soon the blue sea appears and the roofs of the little village down by the shore. "Now we shan't be long," says Cap'n Binnacle.

To Rupert's surprise Cap'n Binnacle does not stop in the village but drives on to the high ground beyond. Then he points towards the headland. "That's the most likely place to meet your fish," he says. Rupert clambers right to the edge of the sea. "I'd better stand up so that the jumping fish can see me," he thinks. "Hallo, there is a fish coming, but he is a much larger one. The big fish makes straight for him. "Are you Rupert Bear?" he asks. "If so, I've come to carry you to the sea-serpent."

RUPERT GETS A BOAT

He says, "If you will come with me,
I'll carry you right out to sea."

The puffins have a good idea,
To use a boat they've seen quite near.

Now Rupert finds it's just a shell,
But as a boat it should do well.

Just then the Captain comes in sight,
He thinks the shell will be all right.

Rupert gazes at the big fish in consternation. "But if you carried me to the sea-serpent I should get awfully wet," he says. "If we got a little boat you could pull it." The fish looks doubtful and neither of them notices that two puffins are listening to their conversation. Just then one of the puffins chips in. "If the boat was tiny enough the fish could pull it. I know just the thing. Come with us, little bear, and have a look." So Rupert follows the puffins across the rocks to a distant part of the shore.

The two birds alight on a rock near an enormous shell. "There," says one of the puffins, "that's the lightest boat that you will get." Then the little bear gets up with a smile. "Why, of course," he says, "I must ask Cap'n Binnacle." He starts back over the rocks and finds to his joy that the Cap'n has started to search for him. There's a big fish who is going to take me to the sea-serpent," he cries. "We've found a shell here. Do you think that you can make it so that it won't sink?"

RUPERT GOES TO SEA

He fixes floats all round the rim,
Then says, "I think that's pretty trim!"

The jumping fish comes back to ask,
If they have almost done their task.

He says that he will test the boat,
And so, with care, they let it float.

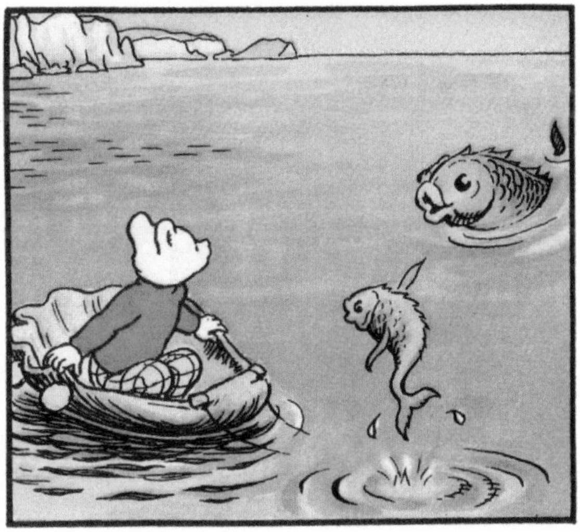

The great fish bustles up to know,
If Rupert's ready now to go.

The old Cap'n stares in astonishment at the great shell. "You do get the maddest ideas, young Rupert," he says. Stringing some corks on to a long cord he puts them round under the rim of the shell and clips the cord to the edge. "There, Rupert," he says, "even if the shell does fill with water it can't sink." Rupert tows it through the water and the jumping fish suddenly leaps up in front of him. "How topping," pipes the little creature. "I could pull that myself."

The jumping fish seizes the two cords and, swimming under the water, pulls the shell with Rupert inside it round the shore, while the old Cap'n keeps pace along the rocks looking as excited as the little bear himself. Suddenly the big fish appears again. "Now for it," thinks Rupert, trembling a little. "We mustn't waste any more time," says the jumping fish, leaping out of the water again. "Hold tight to the edge of the shell, little bear, and don't be frightened. We shall go very fast."

RUPERT MEETS THE SERPENT

Their speed fills Rupert with alarm,
But on they go and meet no harm.

A serpent calls as they draw near,
"My daddy will be glad you're here."

And then he swims away quite fast,
To say that Rupert's here at last.

The serpent soon comes back again,
And brings his father to explain.

The great fish looks at the shell and seems quite satisfied. Seizing the cord he sets off at a tremendous speed that nearly takes Rupert's breath away. "Those must be the islands," he thinks, "and still I don't know why the sea-serpent wants me in such a hurry!" The jumping fish becomes very active. Leaping on to a rock he makes a high-pitched noise and at once a long, lithe creature comes up from the sea. "Good gracious, it's not the old sea-serpent. It must be a young one," gasps Rupert.

After a moment's talk the young sea-serpent makes off. "We shan't be long now," says the fish. "The sea-serpent's gone to fetch his daddy!" Soon the young sea-serpent returns bringing the old one with him. "Ah, Rupert," says the great creature, "how good of you to come. Last week I found a very friendly little person and brought him here as a companion for my son, but he's not at all well." Rupert looks puzzled. "But why send for me?" he asks.

RUPERT FINDS AN OLD FRIEND

He says, "A friend of yours is ill,
And you can help him if you will."

They reach another island soon,
And hurry to a small lagoon.

"Who can it be?" thinks Rupert Bear,
Then finds the merboy lying there.

"Quick," Rupert cries, "he may get worse;
Please fetch a doctor or a nurse."

The sea-serpent smiles indulgently at Rupert's question. "I sent for you because the little person who is ill knows you and he thinks that you are very clever." Bending his long neck, he takes hold of Rupert firmly by the back of his jersey and, holding him high in the air he swims away. After another rapid journey Rupert finds himself above some rocks at the edge of another island. The old sea-serpent can't speak but the young one joins in. "There's my little pal over there," he says.

"Why, it's the merboy!" Rupert cries. "What's the matter? Have you got a pain?" "I'm so weak," whispers the little merboy, "I can't move or swim. I think I must be going to die." Rupert is quite frightened and runs back to the rocks. "It's my pal the merboy," cries the little bear. "He really is ill and I've no idea what's the matter with him. Have you tried to find a mer-doctor?" "Good gracious!" says the big sea-serpent, "are there such people? I'll start at once!"

RUPERT GOES FOR FOOD

The serpent says, "I won't delay,"
And goes to find one straight away.

For fruit now Rupert looks around,
But nuts are all that can be found.

To crack the nuts the serpent tries,
"They're much too hard to break," he sighs.

They try to tempt the merboy, but
He doesn't want to eat a nut.

Rupert watches the old sea-serpent swim out to sea and disappear under the water in his search, but the young one won't leave the island and stays gazing at his sick friend. Rupert decides to see what food he can find. In the upper part of the island he catches sight of a tree with dark blobs hanging in it. A parrot calls to him cheerfully. "Are those things eatable?" asks Rupert. "I should think they are!" squawks the parrot. "I've lived on them all my life and I'm over a hundred years old."

Rupert offers them to the young serpent who takes a nut but cannot crack it. "It's my opinion that you would have to be jolly strong to eat that thing at all," he grunts; " 'tis just like biting a pebble." Rupert is worried. He goes to the merboy and gently shakes him. "Would you like to try a nut if I break it for you?" he asks. The merboy waves the nut away. "You're very kind, Rupert," he whispers, "but I've had plenty to eat." "Oh dear," says Rupert, as the merboy falls asleep again.

RUPERT SOLVES THE PUZZLE

The serpent comes back, looking glum,
He's found nobody who can come.

"It's hot," says Rupert, "so I think
I'll ask him if he wants a drink."

Then Rupert gives a joyful shout,
And starts to dance and jump about.

"I know what's wrong!" he cries with glee,
"I've got to get you in the sea."

Before long the old serpent appears. "Have you found a mer-doctor?" asks Rupert anxiously. The sea-serpent looks glum. "I can't find a mer-doctor," he says. "It's no good, little bear, you're our only hope." Rupert is very worried. He turns slowly towards the small lagoon and thinks hard. "The merboy is not weak because he is hungry," he murmurs. "Perhaps he is thirsty. I wonder if this water is drinkable. It looks lovely and clear." Kneeling on a stone he tastes it.

Suddenly the two sea-serpents see him give a jump and a shout and begin to dance about in the greatest excitement. "I've got it!" he shouts. "I'm sure I'm right." The old sea-serpent stares in astonishment. "That's very satisfactory," he says, "but what are you talking about?" Rupert scampers to the merboy and insists on him sitting up. "You must leave here quickly," he cries. "I've found your trouble. You're a salt water merboy and this is fresh water. You might have died."

RUPERT SENDS FOR HIS BOAT

The merboy cannot walk, and so
On Rupert's back he has to go.

He soon begins to feel all right,
While Rupert watches with delight.

The serpents praise the little bear,
But Rupert starts to scold the pair.

He sends them off to fetch the shell,
To take him home now all is well.

Rupert urges the merboy to get down to the sea, but without success. "I'm too weak for anything," whispers the little creature. "Do you think you could carry me, Rupert?" So Rupert starts the dangerous descent over the rocks with the merboy on his back. Rupert's perilous journey ends safely and in a few moments the merboy gives a happy smile. "Why, I feel better already!" he cries. He begins to dive and frolic around, while the little jumping fish comes to see what it is all about.

The sea-serpents are astonished and move round to tell Rupert how clever he is. "It was very bad of you to put a salt-water merboy in a fresh-water pool. I think you had better let him go home at once." The sea-serpents are not used to being scolded, and look comically bewildered. "Fetch my shell-boat," says the little bear. "Then the big fish can take us to our homes." As the great creatures move off the little jumping fish gazes at Rupert. "You have got a nerve talking to the sea-serpents like that."

RUPERT RIDES HOME

They soon come back and bring the fish,
As Rupert and the merboy wish.

The shell-boat starts upon its way,
To take them back to Rocky Bay.

The Captain waits to see them come,
And how he stares at Rupert's chum.

"Well!" Mrs. Bear says to her son,
"I thought that it was just your fun."

Rupert and the merboy watch the procession coming in. "Sea-serpents are rather odd, aren't they?" says the little bear, "they seem quite kindly people." The two sea-serpents promise Rupert that they will not take the merboy away from his home any more and they thank him for all he has done. Then they and the jumping fish go with him as far as the last of the serpentine islands to see the great fish start his journey back to Rocky Bay.

Cap'n Binnacle is watching for Rupert's return and very soon the little bear is standing on the rock beside him. "Bless my soul," he cries, "you've brought back a merboy. You must let me keep this shell-boat among my treasures, Rupert." When the merboy has said good-bye and swum away, Cap'n Binnacle gets out his rattly old car and drives the little bear back to Nutwood. Soon he is pouring out the story of his adventure since he first saw the jumping fish.

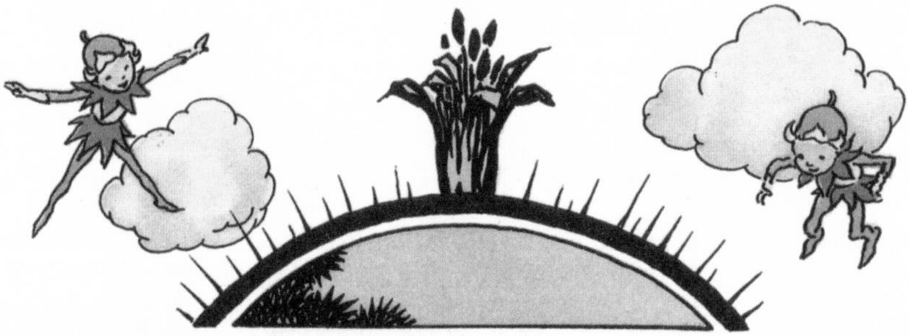

RUPERT and the GOOSEBERRY FOOL

Telling what happens when Rupert meets an imp with the wrong idea of a joke

RUPERT TRIES HIS NEW SWING

"Oh, thank you," Rupert shouts with glee,
"This swing is just the thing for me."

When later, Willie Mouse he spies,
"Come in, and have a swing," he cries.

Young Willie says he'd love to try,
And soon he's swinging very high.

The rope gets caught up on a bough,
But Willie saves himself somehow.

Mr. Bear has been busy making a fine new swing for Rupert's birthday and has found a clear place in the orchard just big enough to take it. "There, now you'll be able to amuse yourself for hours and it may keep you out of mischief," he smiles. Rupert is delighted and his first thought is to share it with his pals so, after trying the swing, he runs to the gate just in time to see Willie the mouse going past with a shopping basket. "Hi, Willie, come and see my new present!" he cries.

Willie turns as Rupert calls and, putting down the shopping basket, is soon installed in the new swing. "Just hold tight and I'll give you a push," says Rupert. "I say, this is fine, aren't you lucky!" cries the little mouse as he goes higher and higher and close to the leaves of an apple tree. All at once one of the branches starts to move slightly. It catches the near side rope and stops the swing suddenly so that Willie has to grab the other rope to save himself from falling.

RUPERT CHASES THE RUNAWAY

The little mouse has had a fright,
But otherwise he is all right.

"Look in that tree!" gasps Rupert Bear,
"What is that queer thing, grinning there?"

And now it jumps down from the tree,
The strangest creature you could see.

"Come on!" and Rupert starts to run,
"Let's catch him up and have some fun."

Still clutching the rope Willie lets himself down and stands there looking rather shaken. "Good gracious, are you all right? How did it happen?" asks the little bear anxiously. "I don't know. I suppose the swing went crookedly," says Willie. "It didn't seem to," answers Rupert. "And it certainly didn't do that when I was using it." Feeling very puzzled they gaze up into the apple tree. Then they start with surprise, for a strange creature is grinning from between the leaves.

While Rupert and Willie gaze upwards, the face in the apple tree disappears and there is a rustle among the leaves. Next minute a small figure drops lightly to the ground and darts away. He has a large head and carries a stick with a small bladder at the end of it. "Here, quick, let's follow him," cries Rupert, setting off in pursuit, while Willie picks up his basket and tries to keep pace. Reaching the Common they are just in time to see the little creature leap into the middle of a bramble patch.

RUPERT AND WILLIE GO WALKING

They trail him to a bramble patch,
Where all the tendrils tear and scratch.

A chuckle makes them turn, and find
The little creature just behind.

The chums are close enough to see,
His head is like a gooseberry.

He seems to like them both, and so
To take a little walk they go.

Determined to find out who the mysterious stranger is, Rupert and Willie press forward; but no sooner do they reach the edge of the bramble patch than, without warning, long trailers and tendrils stretch out to trip them up. They tumble headlong into the middle of the bush but, to their surprise, they are not scratched. Struggling out they start to pick up the parcels Willie has dropped when they hear a chuckle and see that the little creature is now sitting and laughing at them.

The queer stranger doesn't run away so Rupert and Willie go quite near and find that he has a head just like an enormous gooseberry. "Who on earth are you?" gasps Rupert. "What are you doing here? Is it your fault that the trees and bushes are behaving so queerly?" "Don't you ask me questions," laughs the other, "I'm out for fun. Why not come with me and we'll all have a jolly time together!" He sounds so friendly that the two pals smile and let him lead them for a walk.

RUPERT FINDS PODGY PIG

"Now I must go," says Willie Mouse,
"And take this shopping to my house."

Then Rupert finds his friend has found
Fat Podgy, lying on the ground.

"Don't wake him!" says the little man.
"I'll play a joke now, if I can."

He waves his stick round in the air,
Which greatly puzzles Rupert Bear.

During their walk Rupert and Willie try to find out who their little companion is, but he will tell them nothing and at length Willie declares that he must hurry home with his shopping basket. The little stranger pays no attention but peers through a gap in the hedge and a wide smile spreads over his gooseberry face. Next moment he darts through, and Rupert, scrambling in pursuit, finds him standing and gazing at the still figure of Podgy Pig who is comfortably sleeping in the bright sunshine.

As Rupert runs towards him the queer little stranger holds up a finger and asks him to be quite quiet. "I told you I was out for fun," he whispers, "well, here's a wonderful chance for a joke. Just sit down for a minute and watch me." He moves silently towards the sleeping figure of Podgy and walks slowly round him making curious signs and waving his stick with the bladder on the end. Rupert looks on with a puzzled expression. "What ever does he think he's doing?" he murmurs.

RUPERT GETS VERY ANNOYED

Then very pleased with what he's done,
He hurries back to watch the fun.

A gorse bush suddenly pops out,
And Podgy wakes up with a shout.

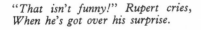

"That isn't funny!" Rupert cries,
When he's got over his surprise.

The cheeky creature pays no heed,
But runs round Rupert at great speed.

The little stranger quickly returns to Rupert and dances about with joy. "Now you'll see something," he cries. "Oh my, you *will* laugh!" At that moment an extraordinary thing happens, for a gorse bush suddenly springs to life under the unconscious Podgy and carries him up with it. The little pig wakes with a start. "Hi, where am I? What's happened?" he gasps. He struggles to get up, but every time he moves the prickles stick into him and he has to keep quite still.

The sight of Podgy Pig caught on top of the gorse bush and unable to get down makes the little stranger shake with laughter, but Rupert is very annoyed. "If that's your idea of a joke it isn't mine!" he exclaims. "Listen to poor old Podgy crying out. Those prickles must be hurting him. If you made that gorse bush grow just you take it away at once!" But the small creature only laughs the more and starts running round him in circles so fast that Rupert gets quite giddy.

RUPERT TALKS TO THE IMP

Another bush springs into sight,
Puts Rupert in the same, sad plight.

The little creature bounds away,
And leaves the chums in great dismay.

An Imp of Spring comes out to see,
What's going on so near his tree.

He hurries to the little bear,
Who tells him how he got in there.

While the little stranger has been running round he has been waving his stick and suddenly another gorse bush springs up hemming Rupert in a tight circle of sharp spikes. "Ha-ha, I'll teach you to start giving me orders," he cries, grinning all over his gooseberry face. "Ho-ho, this is the best joke I've had for ages. Now good-bye. Get out of that if you can!" He bounds away and is lost to sight in a twinkling, leaving Rupert and Podgy staring at each other across the field.

After the stranger has disappeared there is a commotion at the base of a large tree and through a hollow crack there appears one of the Imps of Spring. "What's going on here?" he demands. "Why have these roots appeared down below?" He spies the gorse bushes, and darting across the grass he leaps up and balances lightly on the prickles. "And what are *you* up to?" he cries. "I didn't do it!" says Rupert indignantly. "It was done by a little chap about your size with a gooseberry face."

RUPERT IS GIVEN A WHISTLE

The Imp tells Rupert, "Have no fear!
I'll make those bushes disappear."

He says, "I know who did this thing;
That creature is an Imp of Spring!"

He is their Jester, bright and gay,
But all that day he's been away.

The Imp says, "Take this whistle, please,"
And Rupert, rather cross, agrees.

At Rupert's words the little man shows every sign of excitement. Leaping to the ground he grabs a wand from his wallet and waves it. Immediately Rupert's gorse bush disappears, the prickles flying off in all directions and the next minute the other bush is treated in the same way so that Podgy lands in the grass with a bump. "Did you say he had a face like a gooseberry?" cries the Imp. "That must be the Gooseberry Fool. He's one of us. He's been missing all day. Which way did he go?"

While he and Rupert are recovering from their shock Podgy asks who the Gooseberry Fool is. "Why, he's our King's Jester," says the Imp. "His job is to make jokes all day and make the King laugh. We can't work half so well when he isn't there. He's not supposed to come up here, but he's full of mischief and does things without permission. We do want him back." "H'm, I don't think much of his jokes!" says Rupert ruefully. But the Imp only feels in his wallet and hands him a tiny whistle.

RUPERT GIVES THE SIGNAL

They are to blow with all their might,
Should that young Jester come in sight.

"Come on, let's find him!" Rupert cries,
"Before some other tricks he tries."

They meet the Jester Imp once more,
And he's as cheeky as before.

He makes the grass grow very tall,
Until the chums can't move at all.

The Imp returns into the hollow tree. "We *must* get that Gooseberry Fool back," he says, "we're all too busy to come and look for him, but if you see him anywhere do please blow that little whistle and we'll be there in a flash to take him home." He disappears and the two pals stare after him. "Come on, let's find the little creature before he does any more mischief," says Rupert, and though Podgy is still scared they start to search in the direction where they last saw the Gooseberry Fool.

After about ten minutes the two pals reach the end of their search, for the Gooseberry Fool himself pops out from behind a tree. "Good gracious, you two *are* clever!" he cries cheerfully. "How did you get away from that gorse? Would you like to see another joke? Here's a lovely one. Look." He waves his stick and at once the grass and weeds shoot up around Rupert and Podgy, so thick that they cannot move their feet. Just in time Rupert raises the whistle and blows a shrill note.

RUPERT TELLS STORY TO WILLIE

But Rupert calls the Imps along,
And out they come to see what's wrong.

They rescue Rupert and his chum,
Who are so glad the Imps have come.

"Good-bye!" the little creatures say,
Then quickly vanish right away.

When Willie comes their way again,
These strange adventures they explain.

The Gooseberry Fool chuckles to see Rupert and Podgy again helpless. But the whistle has done its work. Hardly have its echoes died when Imps of Spring appear and, leaping upon the mischievous creature, they carry him back to his underground work. Then the Imp with the wallet again produces his wand and next minute the tall grass and weeds shrivel away and the two pals are free. "Well, I'm glad you all came so quickly," gasps Rupert. "I never knew grass could be so strong!"

While Rupert and Podgy are gazing at the hollow where the Imps have disappeared Willie, who has finished his work, runs to them and they tell him the queer story. "My, it was lucky that you had to go home!" says Rupert. "You wouldn't have enjoyed what we went through. That Gooseberry Fool had a queer idea of what was funny!" "Never mind," grins Podgy, "the gorse didn't hurt so long as we kept still and the tall grasses didn't do us any harm. We're none the worse for it, so why worry?"

RUPERT'S SWING

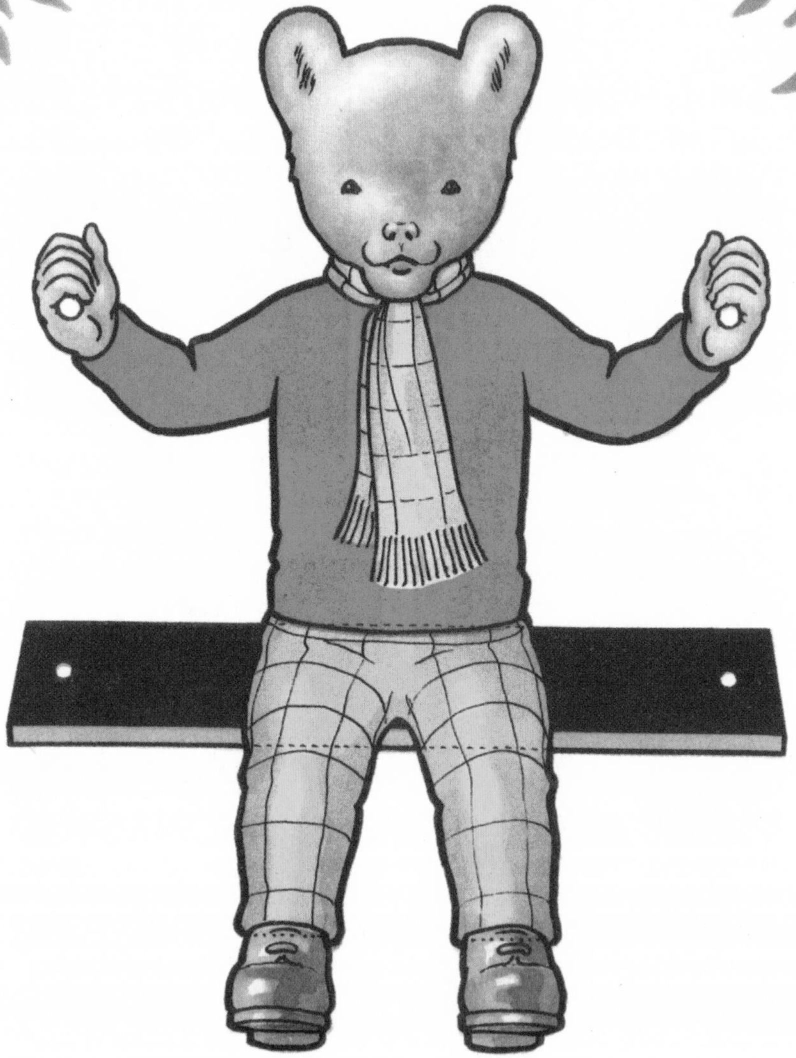

Would you like to make Rupert on a swing? Then trace or copy this figure on a stiff paper or thin card and cut it out carefully. Next pierce the holes, two in the seat and two in the hands. Finally take a piece of thin string about 18 inches long, pass it through the four holes and knot the ends or tie them together behind the seat. To make it more life-like, bend the body and the knees and the feet along the dotted lines.

RUPERT and the PAPER 'PLANE

How Bingo's craze for model making saved Rupert and made Bill eager to learn.

RUPERT MEETS THE SQUIRE

Our little bear one day sets out,
To sketch the country round about.

A gentleman is walking there,
And stops to speak to Rupert Bear.

He sees the drawing with surprise,
"I own that tower you've sketched," he cries.

The Squire tells Rupert that he may,
Go up the tower that very day.

Rupert has had a parcel from his Uncle Bruno and in it he finds a large sketch book, some crayons and a pencil. In great delight he asks permission and runs out to find something to draw. After a long walk he spies a lonely tower. "That should be easy and should look nice," he murmurs, and sitting down on a convenient stone he is soon so absorbed that he doesn't notice a stranger approaching until a genial voice makes him start and jump up in a fluster.

The stranger looks at Rupert's drawing gravely. "So you decided to sketch my tower? It's quite a good picture," he declares. "Is it your tower?" asks Rupert excitedly. "Then you must be the squire of these parts!" "That is correct," agrees the gentleman; "and that tower has been in my family for hundreds of years. It's empty at the moment. There's a wonderful view from the top. Would you like to go up to the roof and get another sketch from there? It's quite safe if you go carefully."

RUPERT INVITES BILL AND BINGO

"How lovely!" Rupert cries with glee,
And quickly takes the tiny key.

He hurries off in great delight,
Till Bill and Bingo come in sight.

"Come here!" calls Bingo, "I'll explain,
How you can make a paper 'plane."

Cries Rupert, as he waves the key,
"Who's coming up the Tower with me?"

At the squire's offer Rupert jumps up and down in excitement. "Very well, then," smiles the other, "here is the key. It's a very tiny one for so large a tower so take great care of it. I have to be away until to-morrow. You can come and give it back to me then." Thanking him, Rupert hurries happily away to find some pals who will come with him. Before long he comes across Bill Badger and Bingo the brainy pup, who are standing and looking rather earnestly at something Bingo is holding.

As Rupert joins his pals Bingo turns to him. "Hello, Rupert," he says. "I've just found how to fold a paper 'plane and I was showing it to Bill. Look, here it is." He launches the little shape into the air and it glides steadily away before settling on the grass. They play with it for a while and then the little bear tells his story ". . . and so I've got the key of that lovely tower," he says. "Will you both come with me and explore it?" "How topping, of course I will," cries Bingo.

RUPERT LEAVES BILL BEHIND

Bill says, "I have a job to do;
But I'll be quick, then join you two."

To this they all agree, and so
Off to the ancient Tower they go.

The chums are eager to explore,
So Rupert opens up the door.

"It's rather creepy," sighs the pup,
But Rupert says, "We must go up."

As Rupert and Bingo wait, Bill makes his decision. "I'm supposed to be running an errand for my Daddy," he says, "I must finish that first. You go on and I'll come back and join you as soon as I can." He hurries away and the other two make their way towards the tower. As they near it they find that they are walking through grass that is deep and uncut. "What a topping place," says Rupert; "look at that moat and the drawbridge." "Yes, it's a very lovely spot," says Bingo.

Carefully taking the tiny key from his pocket Rupert finds it fits and the next minute he and Bingo are inside the tower. "Why this place is completely bare," he says. "It looks a bit creepy to me," says Bingo. "Don't be silly," says Rupert. "The Squire wouldn't have sent us here if there had been anything wrong with it. Close the door in case anyone else comes. We can open it again for Bill." The door shuts and the pals start up the iron spiral staircase before them.

RUPERT SPIES BILL IN THE DISTANCE

They climb the stairs, then when these stop,
A ladder leads right to the top.

At last they get there, safe and sound,
And they can see for miles around.

"Look there!" says Rupert, "on that hill,
That tiny figure looks like Bill."

"I'll let him in," says Bingo now,
And then the knob comes off, somehow.

The inside of the tower is a curious place. The iron spiral staircase leads to the first floor and then one wooden ladder after another leads them higher. Rupert finds it hard to carry his sketch book while he is climbing but, by being very cautious, he at last reaches the top and steps out on to the roof. "Whew! thank goodness we're here," he says; "what a grand view. It's worth the climb." All at once he pauses and looks curiously at the door. "I say, what wobbly handles these are," he murmurs.

Rupert runs to the parapet and gazes across the countryside. "Just look at that view. Isn't it wonderful!" he cries. "The Squire said that I might do a sketch of it, but I'm sure I could never draw that. I'm not half clever enough." Suddenly he spies a tiny figure far off. "Why there's Bill already," he says. "Let's go down and let him in." Bingo runs back to the roof door. Then Rupert hears a rattling noise and sees his pal staring at something in his hand. "What's up?" he asks.

Rupert and the Paper 'Plane

RUPERT AND BINGO ARE TRAPPED

*"Don't fret," says Rupert with a grin,
"We soon can fix the handle in."*

*But now the spindle falls right through,
"Oh dear," they sigh, "what shall we do."*

*The chums are really trapped up there,
"Let's look for Bill," says Rupert Bear.*

*Bill Badger comes on at a run,
For now, he thinks, he'll join the fun.*

Rupert finds Bingo gazing in bewilderment at something shining. "It's the handle of the door. It came away in my hand," says the Pup. "Well, don't look so worried," laughs Rupert. "All you have to do is to stick it back on its spindle again. There should be a little screw somewhere. I expect its fallen on the floor." Bingo tries to do as Rupert has said, but he is rather clumsy and instead of fitting the handle on neatly he manages to push the spindle right through the door.

The two pals gaze at each other in dismay as they hear the spindle with its other handle clatter down the ladder and crash on the landing below. "How awful, we can't open the door. We're trapped!" cries Rupert. They rush to the parapet and see that Bill is rapidly approaching. "We'll tell him what has happened," says Bingo. "If you throw him the key he can open the main door and come and rescue us." "I daren't," groans Rupert. "It would fall into the moat or long grass and he'd never find it."

RUPERT HAS A GRAND IDEA

But Rupert waves and starts to shout,
To tell Bill what it's all about.

Then Bingo hears his chum explain,
That he must make a paper 'plane.

The 'plane will carry down the key,
Then Bill can come and set them free.

Says Bingo then, "I like your plan;
I'll make the strongest 'plane I can."

Rupert spends some time shouting down to Bill and explaining how they are trapped. Then he returns to Bingo, who is wandering about in anxiety. "Bill wants to run back and see if the Squire has another key," he says, "but that wouldn't do. The Squire will be away until to-morrow." All at once he pauses and looks excited. "I do believe I've got an idea," he smiles. "D'you remember what you were doing when I met you? You were making a paper 'plane. Could you make another?"

Rupert goes on with his idea. "This sketch book of mine is big and the paper is very strong and thin. Would it make a 'plane large enough to carry the key down to Bill?" Bingo quickly looks more cheerful. "It's a wonderful idea if you think we could put the key on safely," he breathes. "Well, we can only try," says Rupert. He picks up his new sketch book and carefully tears out one of the pages and Bingo kneels to start the folding. "I must watch this; it looks clever," says the little bear.

RUPERT LAUNCHES THE 'PLANE

Quite soon it's ready now to fly,
But down it falls, when first they try.

So Rupert ties the key below,
And now the tiny 'plane will go.

When Rupert starts the 'plane with care,
It glides, quite safely, through the air.

The key is soon picked up by Bill,
Who thinks the whole thing such a thrill.

Bingo takes great care with the paper 'plane. Finally he tears a little three-sided hole in the tail and shapes the sides of it. "There, that's a good one," he murmurs, as he tries it. Then they push the tiny key into the head of the 'plane but, to their disappointment, it drops straight down and won't travel at all. "Never mind, we won't give up," says Rupert. He pulls a length of cotton out of one of Bingo's cuffs and ties the key farther back under the paper. This time it glides, not very far, but straight.

When all is ready the two pals go back to the parapet. "Thank goodness there isn't a wind," says Rupert. "Oh dear," says Bingo, "I'm feeling so nervous. Suppose anything goes wrong! You send it off, Rupert." So the little bear starts the paper 'plane off on its way. It glides down and down giving a couple of wobbles, righting itself and finally passes right over the head of the excited little badger, landing in a small bush just behind him. Next moment Bill has run to the door.

RUPERT AND BINGO ARE RESCUED

When Bill gets to the second floor,
He finds the handle of the door.

Poor Rupert gives a thankful sigh,
To hear Bill Badger's cheery cry.

They greet each other with delight,
And quite forget their recent fright.

When Bill has seen the view around,
They leave the tower, homeward bound.

Bill enters the lonely tower and gazes around. "This is a weird place," he mutters. "I wish the others were with me." But he doesn't hesitate. Up the spiral staircase he goes and then up the next ladder and at the foot of the last one he spies what he is searching for. Meanwhile, up on the roof Rupert and Bingo are listening intently. They hear Bill's footsteps and then his cheerful cry as he finds the missing handle. "Hooray, he's found it," cries Rupert. "Now we can get away."

Next minute the spindle appears, the door opens, and Bill Badger is through. "My, it's lucky you didn't come with us," cries Rupert, "we might have all been trapped here for ages!" They take the spindle and both the handles. "We'll give these to the Squire when we return the key," he adds, "he'll be sure to know how to put that door right." They show Bill round the roof and then all set off homewards. "That paper 'plane served you a good turn," says Bill. "You must teach it to me again."

HOW TO MAKE A PAPER 'PLANE

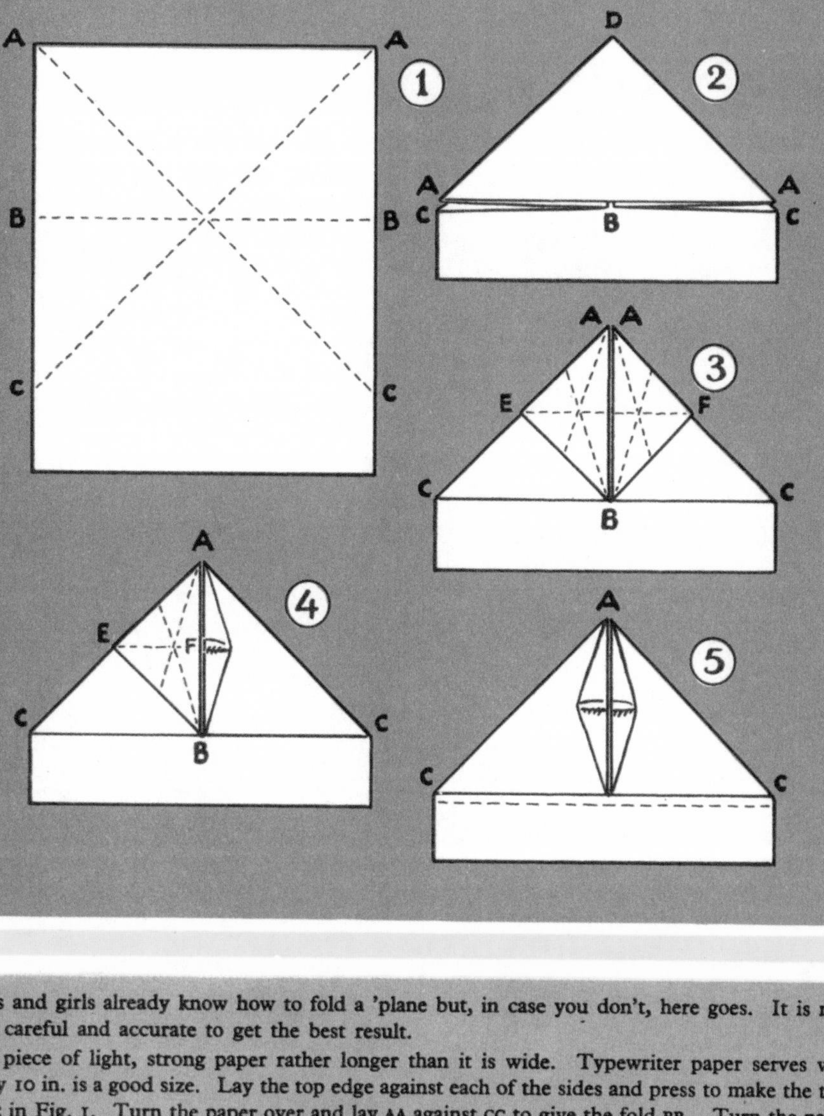

MANY boys and girls already know how to fold a 'plane but, in case you don't, here goes. It is necessary to be very careful and accurate to get the best result.

Take a piece of light, strong paper rather longer than it is wide. Typewriter paper serves very well and 8 in. by 10 in. is a good size. Lay the top edge against each of the sides and press to make the two folds from A to C in Fig. 1. Turn the paper over and lay AA against CC to give the fold BB. Turn the paper back again, bring the points marked "B" together and let the edge AA come down to CC (Fig. 2). Next take the points AA up to D (Fig. 3) and fold the four sides AF, BF, AE and BE, in turn, to the middle line AB; also fold the two points at A down to B. This gives you the necessary folds shown by the dotted lines.

Now for the only tricky bit. Take the two sides AF and BF and put them at the same time against the line AB. This leaves the point F standing up in the air (Fig. 4). Press all folds firmly, making sure that the upright fold comes exactly to F. Treat the point E in the same way to make Fig. 5. Cut off the lower

HOW TO MAKE A PAPER 'PLANE

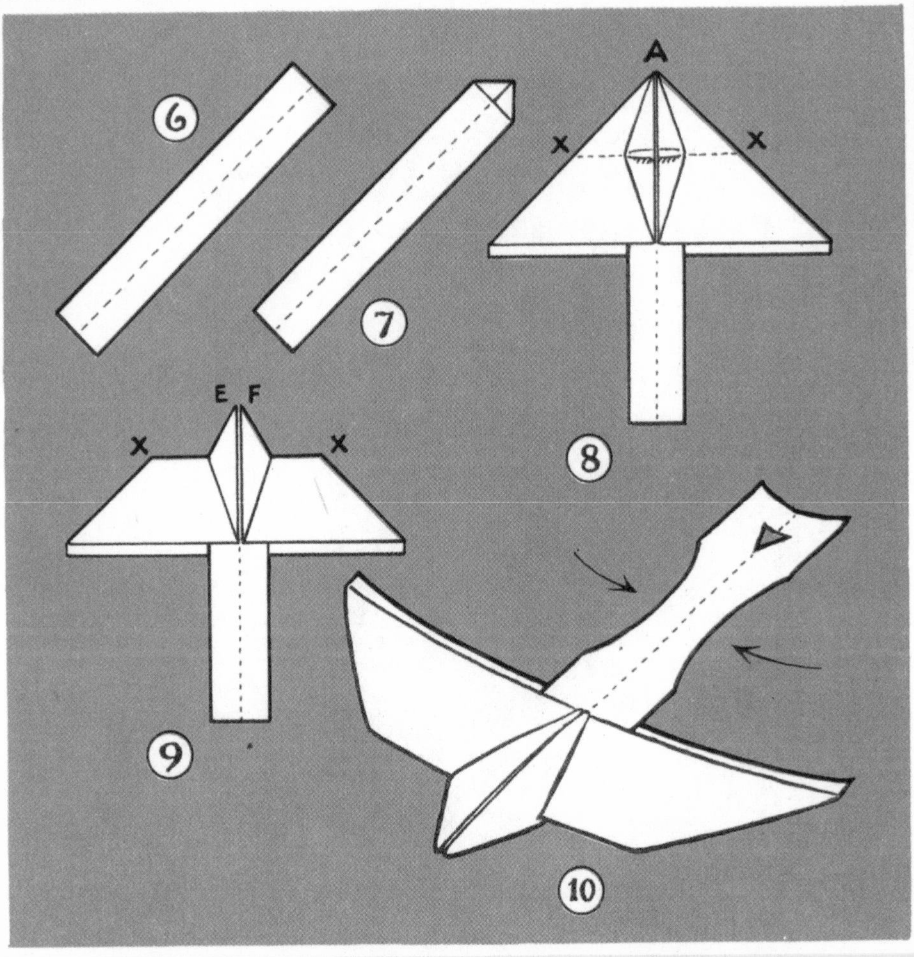

part of the paper along the dotted line a trifle below the line CC. This makes the tail of the 'plane. Fold it in half lengthwise (Fig. 6), press the top corners to the centre line (Fig. 7), and push it into the middle of the 'plane so that the point fits snugly right up into A (Fig. 8).

Lastly, fold the top part of the figure backwards along the line XX. This brings the points E and F into their proper place as the nose of the 'plane (Fig. 9). Again press all the forward folds carefully and hard. The whole thing must now be folded lengthwise to tilt the wings upwards. In particular the tips of both the wings and of the tail must curve up. For launching hold it by the point A (which is now underneath the 'plane) and push it gently forward as you let go. Do not throw it.

If it is tail-heavy try cutting equal curves from each side as shown in Fig. 10. If its gliding is still erratic, cut out a little triangle near the end of the tail as shown. This nearly always steadies the flight.

RUPERT and the THREE GUIDES

Robbery after robbery with the thieves leaving no clues—yet Rupert, with the help of the Guides, solves the mystery.

RUPERT MEETS THE GUIDES

As Rupert rests beneath a tree,
The busy squirrels he can see.

When Rupert calls, they pay no heed,
But scamper off at such a speed.

Then just as Rupert's drawing near,
Three guides, quite suddenly, appear.

They want to find the squirrels too,
So Janet tells them what to do.

Rupert who has wandered to high ground is drowsing beneath a big tree. As he gazes up into the high network of the leaves he sees something moving. "It's a squirrel," he murmurs. "What busy people they are." Rupert calls to the squirrels, but they are in a hurry and scamper off into the forest. "There must be something exciting happening over there," he exclaims. Horace the hedgehog hears him. "If you find out what's the matter do come and tell me," he calls.

Rupert stops suddenly as the smiling faces of three Girl Guides appear over the edge of the bank right in front of him. "Good gracious! Why are you hiding?" he cries. "We're not hiding," laughs the Guide Pauline. "We're stalking the squirrels." "Why that is just what I'm doing too!" says Rupert. "May I join you?" Rupert and the three Guides make their plans. "Let's go straight into the thickest part of the wood," says Janet the Senior Guide.

RUPERT FINDS PODGY

"That man is still," thinks Rupert Bear,
"I wonder what he's doing there?"

Now Rupert hears the gipsy say,
"Strange things are happening to-day."

"Well," Rupert thinks, "that's very queer;
I'll call the guides to come right here."

But Rupert finds they do not come,
And then he meets another chum.

Rupert chooses one way and the three Guides take different directions. All at once he comes across a gipsy standing quite still and staring at a big tree. "What a silent man," thinks Rupert. Screwing up his courage Rupert approaches the man. "Please do you know what's the matter with the squirrels to-day?" asks Rupert. The gipsy turns slowly and gazes vaguely into the depths of the wood. "There will be strange doings in Nutwood this day," he says solemnly.

Rupert repeats his question about the squirrels, and again the gipsy turns and smiles, but he says no more and abruptly strides away into the wood. "Why is he so mysterious?" mutters Rupert. "Hasn't he seen the squirrels? What does he mean by strange things in Nutwood?" Rupert calls several times for Beryl, Janet, and Pauline, but there is no answer. Strolling moodily across the common he sees a little figure kneeling there. "It's Podgy Pig," he says. "I wonder why he is looking so worried."

RUPERT LISTENS TO GAFFER JARGE

It's Podgy Pig, who's kneeling down,
To count his marbles with a frown.

A distant voice calls to the pair,
"It's Gaffer Jarge," says Rupert Bear.

The poor old man is quite dismayed,
Because his tie-pin is mislaid.

So into Nutwood now they go.
For P.C. Growler ought to know.

Trotting over to see his friend Rupert sees that Podgy has spread out a row of marbles and is frowning over them. "Hullo, are you just starting a new game?" asks Rupert. "No, I'm not," moans Podgy. "I've lost one of my marbles. Last night there were a dozen. Now there are only eleven and the one that is gone is the best one." To cheer his pal up, the little bear tells him of the queer behaviour of the squirrels and asks him to come and help the three Guides in their search.

The two little pals find Gaffer Jarge very hot and breathless. "Hey, young Rupert," wheezes the old man, "be a good lad and find Constable Growler. Somebody's stolen my diamond tie-pin from my bedroom." "Poor old Gaffer," cries Rupert. "Of course we'll find the Constable at once." Podgy, forgetting his own loss, runs off with him, down the slope from the common. "Why, there is the Constable!" cries Podgy. "He looks busy. I wonder what those two ladies are talking to him about."

RUPERT WARNS HIS MOTHER

A ring and brooch are missing too,
And no one knows just what to do.

Now more and more arrive to tell,
That they have lost some things as well.

So Rupert runs to Mrs. Bear,
To make quite sure her pearls are there.

"They've gone!" she cries in great alarm,
"I hope they will not come to harm."

As Rupert and Podgy dash up to the little group Mrs. Pug and Mrs. Sheep turn to see what all the excitement is about. Rupert breathlessly tells about Gaffer Jarge's loss. Constable Growler stares at them. "What, another thing missing!" he cries. "Whatever has come over the village? Half the houses have lost something." More and more people come to tell of things that they have lost, mostly pieces of jewellery, and finally Gaffer Jarge hobbles up. "This is getting serious," declares the Constable.

Rupert finds his mother hanging out the clothes and he pours out the story of all the things that have disappeared. "Thank goodness I haven't lost anything," says Mrs. Bear. "You'd better make sure," says Rupert. Mrs. Bear looks anxious. "I left my string of pearls on the side of my dressing-table mirror and I take it for granted that they are safe," she says, "but if there's a thief about we'd better make sure." Hurrying to the bedroom, she gives a gasp. "My pearls, they've gone!" she cries.

RUPERT TELLS THE POLICEMAN

Now Rupert's Daddy comes along,
And they must tell him what is wrong.

When Rupert meets the guide again,
About the thefts he must explain.

She says, "I'll come along with you,
I've lost some silver paper too."

So off they run without delay,
And meet with Podgy on the way.

She bustles around and puts on her coat and starts off for the village. "Look, Mummy, here's Daddy," says Rupert. "Stay and get his tea and tell him all about it. I can run back and ask Constable Growler to add your pearls to his list." Taking a short cut he suddenly meets Guide Janet. "Hullo, Rupert," she calls. "Did you have any luck with those squirrels?" "Good gracious, I'd forgotten all about the squirrels," cries Rupert. And he tells her of the mysterious things that have happened.

The Guide Janet gets excited as Rupert tells his story. "If you're going to the Constable, I'll come with you," she declares. "I've lost something, too. I collected a lot of silver paper and kept it in my room and this morning it had vanished! Come on. We'd better hurry." As they near the cottage Rupert and Janet meet Podgy Pig again. "Hi, Podgy," puffs Rupert. "We're just off to tell the Constable of more things that have vanished. Why not come and tell him about your missing marble."

RUPERT SPIES A GIPSY

The constable gets out his list,
Of all the things that have been missed.

He's very worried by this news,
For, up to now, he has no clues.

The chums would like to find a plan,
To catch the robber if they can.

So Rupert wanders on once more,
And meets the man he saw before.

The three friends rush into the Constable's cottage and Rupert tells him that his mother's pearls have vanished. The Constable adds them to the list, but when Janet and Podgy tell him about the silver paper and the missing marble he looks stern. "Now then," he growls, "are you trying to make fun of me?" Constable Growler follows the three friends outside and scratches his head. "I can't make head nor tail of it," he says, but Rupert, Podgy, and Janet are already planning what they can do.

Up on the Common the little friends look rather solemn. "We must help the Constable to catch this thief," says Rupert. "But he may be very strong and I don't feel very brave to-day," says Podgy doubtfully. Janet looks excited. "I'd love to try, but I don't know if Guides are supposed to track robbers. I'll find Beryl and ask her." When Janet and Podgy have gone their separate ways Rupert goes back to the wood, and there he spies the tall gipsy collecting wood to take back to his caravan.

RUPERT TACKLES THE GIPSY

To trail the gipsy man he tries,
But he gets caught, to his surprise.

The gipsy laughs and lets him go,
"I didn't steal those things, you know!"

"Go to that tree," he tells the bear,
"You'll find the answer right in there."

Just then a squirrel scurries by,
"I'm late," he mutters with a sigh.

Rupert creeps under the bushes as silently as he can, but very soon he is startled by a loud laugh behind him. "Do you dare to try and trail me, little bear?" cries the man. "You have yet to learn that he who stalks a gipsy generally gets stalked instead." Rupert doesn't try to hide again but lets the man lead him back to the caravan. "What's your trouble now?" asks the gipsy, smiling kindly at him. "Oh, it's something important," cries Rupert. And he tells of all the things that are missing in Nutwood.

From the twinkle in the man's eyes Rupert suspects that he knows something about the affair. The gipsy points to the heart of the forest. "There's no need for you to go back to Nutwood," he says mysteriously. "You can solve all your puzzles by staying where you first met me." When he has spoken the gipsy strides away and leaves Rupert rather bewildered. "I suppose that I had better find the tree where I first saw him," he thinks, as he enters the wood.

Rupert and the Three Guides

RUPERT DECIDES TO CLIMB

To find the tree now Rupert tries,
And then the guides again he spies.

"Oh good!" they cry, "we're glad you're here;
We found a tree that's very queer."

They hear a strange noise in the tree,
But it's too dark for them to see.

What can it be? They want to know,
So scrambling up the tree they go.

Rupert gets deeper and deeper into the forest until a chuckle pulls him up sharply. The Guides Beryl and Janet are peeping through the leaves. "Gracious, you made me jump," says Rupert. "What are you doing?" "Well," says Janet, "we're after squirrels again and we've found something queer." Rupert runs with Beryl and Janet until they find the third Guide. "Hello," says Pauline. "Come and listen to this tree." Rupert gazes and then realizes it is the tree where he met the gipsy.

The Guide Pauline doesn't understand, so Rupert explains. "I've been searching for this tree because the gipsy says we'll solve all our puzzles if we come here." They all keep very quiet and sure enough a high-pitched noise seems to keep rising and falling in the topmost branches. The four friends decide to climb up and find out. The first branches are rather high, but Beryl and Janet manage to get on them with Pauline pushing from below; they help Rupert up. Soon they are all scrambling higher and higher.

RUPERT ASKS SOME QUESTIONS

A roof goes right across the top,
So Rupert and the guides must stop.

Now as they wonder what to do,
A swarm of squirrels breaks right through.

A kindly squirrel stops to say,
"Our King was crowned up here to-day."

"What fun!" cries Rupert with delight,
"It must have been a thrilling sight."

As they leave the lower part of the tree they find that it is getting darker and Rupert puts his hand out. "No wonder it's dark," he exclaims, "somebody has joined these top branches and built a sort of roof right across the tree." The three Guides pause and listen to the noise which is now quite close, it swells into a roar and then quite suddenly it stops and there is silence. Next there is a scurrying sound and dozens and dozens of squirrels come streaking downwards.

Rupert calls out and a large squirrel comes across. "Oh do tell us," says Pauline, "what has that crowd been doing up there?" "Didn't you know?" squeaks the little creature. "The King of all squirrels has been crowned to-day and one of our own Nutwood squirrels has been chosen as King." "Well, that's one mystery solved," cries Rupert. "Did you make that beautiful roof across the tree? Can we see where your King was crowned?" The squirrel answered: "I must ask the King first."

RUPERT FINDS THE STOLEN GOODS

The King and both his guards appear,
He says, "Just one *may come up here."*

The roof won't stand much weight, and so
They choose the little bear to go.

The strangest scene meets Rupert's eyes,
And makes him call out with surprise.

The missing things are all around,
How thankful Rupert is they're found.

There is much squeaking and chattering, and through another hole come the King and his two guards. "We never allow strangers at our squirrel crownings but as it is all over now I will allow one of you to go up and see the preparations." The young friends are disappointed, but Rupert turns unselfishly to Beryl. "You're the eldest," he says. Then there is quite an argument until the first squirrel returns and says that the roof is only strong enough for the lightest of them.

Rupert is chosen to go to the top. Soon the little bear is gazing across the platform. "You must have worked hard to make this," cries Rupert. "Did you make that silver throne? And what are all those things sparkling in the sun?" Then he looks closely and gives a cry. "Why, those are my mother's pearls," he shouts, "and up there is Podgy's marble and this chair is covered with Janet's silver paper, and all those rings and diamonds are what have disappeared from Nutwood."

RUPERT PROVES THE GIPSY RIGHT

Now Beryl pops up there to see,
What all the fuss and noise can be.

The squirrel says, "It's quite all right;
We meant to put them back to-night."

"I'll take them," says the little bear,
And wraps them up with greatest care.

They run, for there's no time to lose,
To get to Nutwood with the news.

Rupert has shouted out loud, and next minute Beryl pops her head through the hole in the roof. "We've solved everything," says Rupert. "All those jewels and things are up here. There never was a thief." Beryl at once speaks to Pauline and Janet and collects their handkerchiefs. The squirrel pulls down the ornamental branches, and stripping the jewels from them, he drops them in the handkerchiefs. "Why get so excited?" says the squirrel. "We should have put them all back to-night."

When all the precious things are collected up Rupert joins the three Guides. "Your gipsy was right," says Pauline. "We've found the answer to all our puzzles in this tree." Rupert and the three Guides carefully make their way out of the wood, racing at top speed to Nutwood. Constable Growler turns suspiciously as he hears their voices. "Oh dear, it's those youngsters again," he says. "There are four of them this time. I wonder what trick they are going to play on me now."

RUPERT SURPRISES THE CONSTABLE

To P.C. Growler now they go,
And tell him everything they know.

He listens to their tale with glee,
Then says, "You've done a lot for me."

Now Rupert runs straight home from there,
To take the pearls to Mrs. Bear.

When Rupert meets the guides next day,
Old Gaffer Jarge comes back their way.

Constable Growler's expression soon changes when Rupert is able to tell his story and the Guides hand him the three handkerchiefs. "It's almost unbelievable," says the Constable. "No wonder I couldn't find any clues when there wasn't one thief, but dozens of them. I must take these back to the office," he smiles, "and if you want to do more good turns, go round the village and ask the people to come to me." Rupert asks for his mother's pearls so that he can return them to her himself.

Rupert takes the pearls and scampers home to his mother. She smiles when she sees what is in his hand. "How on earth did you get them back so quickly?" she gasps. "Did you find the thief?" "Lots and lots of thieves," says Rupert. "Not very bad ones. They'd have brought them back to-night, anyway." Next morning the little pals meet to talk about their adventure. "Look, there's old Gaffer Jarge," cries Pauline. "He ought to be pleased this morning, but he doesn't look happy, does he?"

RUPERT FINDS THE TIE-PIN

His tie-pin hasn't been returned,
And he is feeling most concerned.

"I thought I saw it," Rupert sighs,
"I think I did," young Beryl cries.

She says, "It's in the crown, I'm sure,"
And so they hurry back once more.

The poor King says, "What shall I do,
If I give up my gem to you?"

"Hey, young Rupert," wheezes the old man "Where's that tie-pin of mine? I went round to the Constable's house and everything was there, but not mine." Rupert looks very concerned and then hurries to the others. "We haven't done our job properly," he says. Catching sight of a squirrel in the tree he asks if he knows anything about the tie-pin. "If it's lost you won't find it now," says the squirrel. "We've taken that tree roof and the King's chair to pieces." Suddenly Beryl starts to laugh.

"Ask if you can see the King squirrel and I think you'll find that pin!" she says. The squirrel looks doubtful but says, "Go back to where you first saw the King and I'll see if I can find him for you." The Guides push Rupert up into the tree where he finds the King squirrel waiting for him. "There it is in your crown. It's Gaffer Jarge's tie-pin. Oh please give it back to me," says Rupert. The tiny King looks dismayed. "I'll get you a better one," promises Rupert. "I'll have it here in half an hour."

RUPERT RESTORES THE CROWN

Now Rupert tells the squirrel King,
That something just as good he'll bring.

He dashes home again to find,
The little toy he has in mind.

As Rupert quickly runs along,
The hedgehog asks him what is wrong.

"It's beautiful!" the squirrel cries,
And looks at it with shining eyes.

Rupert shows his friends the precious pin. "Now I've got to get busy," he cries. "I've promised to bring the King another jewel within half an hour." The Guide Janet starts forward. "Why not let us take the tie-pin to Gaffer Jarge while you're gone," she says. "We'll race and see who gets back here first." Rupert dashes back to his own cottage. His mother hears him come in and go to his room. "Whatever are you up to?" asks Mrs. Bear. But without answering, Rupert dashes out again.

On the common Rupert meets the three Guides and Horace the hedgehog. "You're just in time to see the end of the affair," he says. Back in the wood Rupert hands his treasure to the King, who squeaks with delight. "What a whopper!" cries the little creature. "It's bigger than the other jewel." "Yes, it's jolly good," says Rupert. "I got it out of a cracker last Christmas." The tiny King leaps away, and Rupert and his three friends are left to tell Horace Hedgehog all about it.

RUPERT and the TRAVEL MACHINE

Adventures come thick and fast to Rupert and Bill Badger when they trespass

RUPERT IS TEMPTED TO TRESPASS

Says Bill, one day, to Rupert Bear,
"I'd like to take a walk in there."

They see a board which says, "Keep out",
And long to know what it's about.

The naughty chums decide to go,
Although it's wrong, as they well know.

The bushes grow so thick and strong,
They find it hard to get along.

Although there has been a heavy fall of snow during the night the day is fine, and the fresh crisp air makes Rupert and Bill Badger decide to go for a long walk into the country. It is not long before they reach the edge of what appears to be a forest. There Bill points to a board which warns all strangers to "keep out". Rupert reads it slowly. "It's funny," he says, "but I've never seen that before. I wonder who could have put it there." "Let's go in," says Bill, "and perhaps we shall find something new."

Rupert hesitates because he doesn't like trespassing, especially when he has been warned to keep out by a brand new notice-board. Bill Badger is in a mischievous mood and before Rupert can stop him he is over the gate, leaving Rupert to follow him. "Hi! wait for me," calls Rupert. But Bill, now determined on his adventure, hurries along with Rupert chasing behind. Very soon they find themselves having a tussle to get through the thick undergrowth that is growing between the huge trees.

RUPERT EXAMINES A MOTOR-CAR

Now as they wonder what to do,
A squirrel asks, "Can I help you?"

He tells them that the road's not far,
So off they run and see a car.

The snow is thick upon the ground,
And yet there are no marks around.

They climb inside, and right away
It starts to move, to their dismay.

After a long time trying to find some sort of path that will at least lead them somewhere, they realize that they are lost. "Now see where your inquisitiveness has landed us," says Rupert. Bill says he is very sorry for getting Rupert in such a fix, when a squirrel hops on to a branch just above their heads and calls out, "Hello, Rupert! Don't worry, I'll show you the way, just follow me." Very soon they see a road running through the forest, and there, to their astonishment, a small motor-car is standing.

The little pals are very puzzled because there are no foot-marks in the snow leading either to or from the car, so Rupert decides to examine their find. "Now who's inquisitive?" asks Bill Badger, as he gingerly peeps over the back while Rupert goes to the car door. "I may be inquisitive," says Rupert, "but only when there is something mysterious. Come on, get in beside me and see how it works." No sooner is Rupert seated at the wheel and Bill is beside him, than the little car starts up on its own.

RUPERT AND BILL ARE TRAPPED

The car goes very fast indeed,
And runs towards a shed at speed.

Just as they fear there'll be a smash,
The doors fly open, with a crash.

At once the heavy doors shut tight,
Which gives the startled chums a fright.

Then suddenly, they start to drop,
"Oh dear," sighs Bill, "I'd like to stop."

Before they can say "Jack Robinson", Rupert and Bill find the car whizzing over the snow-covered road at a rattling good speed. Suddenly Bill points ahead. "Good gracious!" he shouts, "we are going straight for that shed and the doors are closed." Rupert has no time to do anything; the car is now racing too fast for them to jump out. "Hold tight," yells Rupert, "there's going to be an awful crash"; but to their amazement the doors of the shed open, and the little pals find their car is going inside.

As soon as the car is inside the building it stops and the doors close behind them although there is nobody about. "I say," gasps Rupert, "what a funny-looking place, just look at all those chains and pulleys." "Yes, it's funny all right," agreed Bill, "and what's more, we're locked in, so let's get out of the car and explore." Before Rupert can answer there is a whirring sound, and looking over the side Bill cries out, "I say, Rupert, we are sinking through the floor on a sort of lift."

RUPERT RECEIVES AN OFFER

An angry-looking man draws near,
And says, "I mean to keep you here!"

"You trespassed in my wood," says he,
"So now you both must work for me."

The pals are locked up in a room,
And left to mope there, in the gloom.

The cross old man comes back to ask,
If they are ready for their task.

As soon as the lift comes to earth the little pals find themselves in a workshop crammed with funny machinery and, facing them with arms folded on his chest, is an old, white-haired man in overalls. He looks very, very cross and tells them that he has invented that car for the very purpose of catching inquisitive people. "If you hadn't trespassed into my forest you wouldn't be here," he growls, "but as you are, you now stay and work for me," and he leads them away through heavy iron doors.

Rupert and Bill find themselves locked up in a dark room, with only a few boxes and shavings for company, and no hope of escape. "Well," says Rupert, "we really are in a pretty pickle this time. I wonder what they will think at home when we don't turn up to-night." No sooner are the words out of his mouth when the old inventor appears at the door and, speaking through a sort of barred window, tells them that he will set them free if they will agree to test his newly-invented travel machine.

RUPERT AGREES TO TRAVEL

His new machine they have to test,
And Rupert says, "We'll do our best."

The man now finds a bright, red charm,
And straps it tight on Rupert's arm.

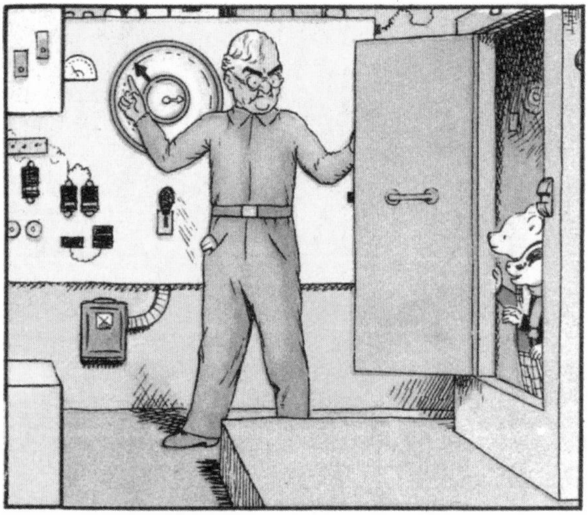

When they are in the huge, steel box,
The old man fastens all the locks.

They're off! and whizzing round and round,
For South Sea Islands they are bound.

Rupert asks to see the machine; so the inventor leads the two little pals into his workshop and shows them what looks like a steel cabinet. "Of course," he says, "you will have to bring something back with you to prove where you have been." "But how shall we be able to get back?" Rupert asks. The old man then fastens something on Rupert's arm that looks like a red seal. "Now," he says "you must both hold tight to each other and then wish to come home. Remember, only one of you need wish."

Into the steel cabinet step Rupert and Bill and they watch as the old man points to the indicator on the wall. "When I close the door," he says, "I shall turn the arrow to point to the South Sea Islands, then I shall press this button and you will be on your way. Now remember both of you, cling tightly together when you wish to come back and only one of you must wish at once." Then he slams the door shut with a bang, touches the button, and the next thing the pals know is they are whizzing into space.

RUPERT MAKES A NEW FRIEND

The little bear lands in a tree,
Which is as soft as it can be.

When Rupert finds he is all right,
He looks for Bill, who's not in sight.

A monkey speaks to Rupert Bear,
And asks him what he's doing there.

"My chum has gone," sighs Rupert now,
"I've got to find poor Bill, somehow."

With a whizz and a bump Rupert lands bang out of the sky on to some large green leaves. For quite a time he lays staring up into space, but as soon as he gets his breath back again he looks around and suddenly realizes that the leaves are those of a palm tree and that he is right at the top. Very carefully he stands upright and gazes around. All he can see is an endless stretch of blue sea with odd little islands dotted about here and there, but there is no sign of Bill Badger anywhere.

Rupert decides that he had better climb down the tree and set off in search of Bill before it gets dark. When he is nearing the ground a friendly looking little monkey says, "Hullo! whoever are you, and where did you come from?" Rupert, having removed his scarf owing to the heat, sits himself down on a rock and starts to fan himself with a palm fan and eat a banana, both of which he found in the palm tree. Feeling cooler and much less hungry he tells the monkey about Bill.

RUPERT ASKS THE BIRDS

They call and search all round the place,
But of the badger there's no trace.

The monkey climbs the trees so fast,
That Rupert takes a fall at last.

"Come back!" he calls, "and help me please,
I'm not too good at climbing trees."

"I'll ask these birds," says Rupert Bear,
"If they have seen Bill anywhere."

The monkey says that he hasn't noticed any strangers, but he promises to help Rupert search the island. "Hi! go steady," calls out Rupert. The monkey doesn't seem to hear as he skips along chattering away, his beady little eyes searching everywhere for the missing Bill. Rupert soon finds himself falling down amongst the tropical undergrowth of the island. Somehow he manages to grab hold of a trailing vine-like plant and yell out to his monkey friend for help.

Quickly the monkey leaps from tree to tree and, wrapping his tail around a stout branch, he reaches out a paw to Rupert. "Catch hold," he squeaks, "and if you don't struggle I'll soon have you up beside me." Rupert is astonished at the strength of his little friend and very soon he is sitting on a branch overlooking the whole island. Many lovely coloured birds come to see what is the matter, but none of them can help. Suddenly the monkey suggests that possibly Bill is on the larger island.

RUPERT GREETS MR. TURTLE

But now the monkey gives a cry,
"Perhaps he's on that land nearby."

The only way to reach the ground,
Is by a vine that they have found.

As soon as they have reached the shore,
The monkey hurries on before.

He soon returns and with him comes,
A turtle who will help the chums.

From a rocky peak the monkey points to the island and to Rupert and says that he is sure Bill is not on this island. Rupert looks down and is almost dizzy at the great height. "How on earth am I going to get down to the shore?" he asks. "It's all right for you, you can swing from tree to tree, but I cannot." The monkey just grins as he swings away and lowers himself to the shore below. "Come on," cries the monkey, "it's quite safe, grip tight and just let yourself slide down."

Avoiding the dangerous slope Rupert is soon on the shore among all the stones and rocks when he suddenly notices that the monkey is speeding away towards the water. He stands, wondering what to do next when his new-found friend returns with Mr. Turtle. "It's all right, Rupert," says the monkey, "I've told Mr. Turtle all about your little lost friend and he says he will ride you on his back to the other island." Rather startled, Rupert can only stutter out, "Thank you, Mr. Turtle."

RUPERT CROSSES THE WATER

Says Mr. Turtle, "Come with me;
"I'll carry you across the sea."

Just then a bird tells Rupert Bear,
He's seen Bill Badger over there.

The turtle swims so very well,
They feel quite safe upon his shell.

The monkey leaves them both behind,
And runs to see what he can find.

Soon the three are standing on the edge of the water. One look at the sea and Rupert feels too scared to make the crossing. A beautifully coloured bird dives out of the sky. "I say," chirps the bird, "I've just come from the main island and there's such a funny looking animal there that I've never seen before." "By jove!" cries Rupert. "That might be Bill, now I *must* go, Mr. Turtle, if you'll please take me across. I shall never rest until I make sure."

Without any hesitation Mr. Turtle tells Rupert to climb on to his shell. Soon they are on the way with Mr. Turtle swimming as steady as any boat Rupert has ever been on. Quickly they are across the sea and climbing up the beach of the main island. The little monkey skips along ahead with Rupert puffing along behind him and Mr. Turtle clamboring out of the water. "Hi! Rupert!" squeaks the monkey from the top of the cliff, "there's something up here I've never seen before, do hurry up."

RUPERT FINDS BILL ASLEEP

"Look here!" he calls, and Rupert sees
Bill's scarf is hanging in the trees.

Then Rupert finds Bill on the ground,
He seems to be quite safe and sound.

A fearsome islander springs out,
And scares them with his awful shout,

Soon Bill is caught, and Rupert feels
The ground give way beneath his heels.

When Rupert reaches the top of the cliff he looks to where the little monkey is perched on a tree branch pointing to something hanging there. "Why, it's Bill's scarf," cries Rupert. "He must be somewhere about here." After searching for a while they come across Bill Badger, fast asleep. They quickly wake him and he is overjoyed when he sees Rupert. Soon the little bear is pouring out his story of the other island and the wonderful kindness and help of the little monkey and Mr. Turtle.

They are all so excited at the reunion that none of them notice a huge islander approaching through the bushes. All of a sudden the little monkey leaps up into the trees shrieking, "Run, Rupert run. Oh! do run faster." The little pals set off as fast as their legs can carry them with the man panting after them. Just when it looks as though they will be able to escape Bill feels his ankle grabbed and at that minute Rupert finds himself dropping into an animal trap going down, down, down.

RUPERT AND BILL ARE CAPTURED

The islander grins at the bear,
For now he knows he's caught the pair.

The chums are tightly tied with rope,
So to escape they cannot hope.

Poor Bill and Rupert walk so far,
They soon loose track of where they are.

The man soon spies the coloured charm,
That Rupert wears upon his arm.

When Rupert regains his breath and at last clambers to his feet, he looks up and sees Bill in the clutches of the islander, who is now grinning all over his face with the knowledge that he has both of them in his power. First of all, the man ties Bill's hands behind his back; then, having lifted Rupert from the deep pit, he ties him up too. "What do you think he is going to do with us?" quavers Bill. "Cheer up Bill," says Rupert, "we've escaped from worse places than this—keep smiling."

The man seems to keep them walking for miles, but sooner or later they arrive at some rocks. With great strength he takes hold of a huge stone and rolls it to one side. "Oh! Oh!" whispers Rupert, "he's got a cave he's going to shut us up in." Before Bill can say anything the eye of the islander lights on the disc fastened to Rupert's arm. "Gosh! he really seems excited," mutters Bill. "I wonder what he is going to do now." But neither of them can understand the language or his words.

RUPERT LOSES HIS TRAVEL DISC

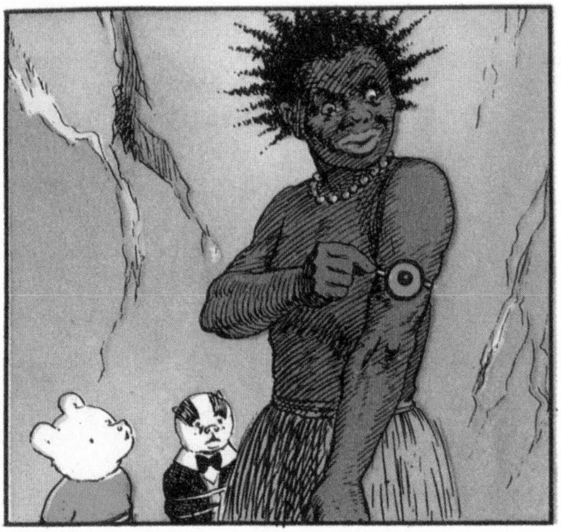

And now, to Rupert's great dismay,
Their captor takes the charm away.

When all is quiet, the monkey comes,
To see if he can help the chums.

The monkey chatters with delight,
While he unties the knots so tight.

Then Rupert has a bright idea,
"I know how we can go from here!"

The brightly coloured disc appeals strongly to the man, so he takes it away from Rupert's arm and fastens it on his own, pointing to it with pride. "That's done it," says Rupert in tones of despair, "we shall never be able to get home now the disc has gone." Soon the man pushes them inside the cave, and to their astonishment they see their little friend the monkey slide down through the roof. "Hello, Rupert," he chatters, "don't worry, I'll soon have you loose."

The little monkey turns Rupert round and starts undoing the string that binds his arms, chattering so excitedly that Rupert can hardly understand what he is saying, but the little bear is very grateful when he finds that both he and Bill are free of their bonds. They creep softly on tiptoe to the mouth of the cave but, to their dismay, they find the islander laid asleep right in their path. Suddenly Rupert's eye catches sight of the disc on the man's arm and a brilliant idea strikes him. He turns to whisper to Bill.

RUPERT RETURNS TO THE SNOW

To Bill he quickly tells his plan,
"We'll test that charm now, if we can."

"'To Nutwood!" shouts the little bear,
And straightway they are in the air.

It's snowy still when they get back,
And land by the inventor's shack.

The old man does not see them there,
Until he's called by Rupert Bear.

"Listen carefully, Bill," Rupert whispers. "You remember what the inventor said, that we must cling tight hold of each other and only one wish." Bill looks very glum. "Yes, but how can we get our disc without waking him?" he asks. "Don't be silly," says Rupert. "If we hang on to him and I make the wish to return we shall all go—now do get ready. Well, here goes—*I WISH TO RETURN TO NUTWOOD.*" Without warning the three of them are whisked up into the air.

When they land it is among all the snow drifted to the side of the road in the forest. Rupert is a little shaken at first, but he cannot restrain a chuckle when he looks at the islander who is sitting dumbfounded, shivering with cold, because he has never seen snow before. Rupert doesn't waste any time, however, and once he is sure that Bill is all right he starts off for the shed with the self-closing doors. Before he has gone very far he sees the inventor, so he starts to run, waving his arms and shouting as he goes.

RUPERT WATCHES THE CHASE

"We're back," cries Rupert, "come and see,
The proof that I have brought with me."

"My word!" the old inventor cries,
"This islander is a surprise."

The islander chases the man,
And so the chums run, while they can.

The old man's workshop is not far,
And there they find the doors ajar.

"Come quickly," gasps Rupert, "we've brought something back from the South Sea Islands for you." The inventor grabs Rupert's arm. "I hope you have," he says. "It will be hard for you if you're playing a trick on me. Dear! dear! You certainly have brought me back a wonderful surprise. I can't understand a word he says." Rupert grins. "We can't help you there," he says, "but we have carried out our part of the bargain, so can we go now, please?"

Before the inventor can answer the islander seems to take a dislike to the old man and chases him through the woods. "What on earth shall we do now?" asks Bill. "We can't run fast enough to catch him up." Rupert pauses a minute and then says, "The inventor is clever enough to look after himself—come along, I've got an idea." Off he starts, running towards the workshop with Bill following at his heels. Good luck is with them, for in his hurry the old man has forgotten to fasten the door.

RUPERT RETURNS TO NUTWOOD

To the controls they find their way,
And set the dials without delay.

Inside the steel box jump the pair,
To start their journey through the air.

Now, once again, they whirl around,
So very far above the ground.

This time they land at Rupert's door,
So thankful to be home once more.

"Whatever are you going to do?" asks Bill nervously. "Just you wait," says Rupert, as he climbs on to a stool in front of the indicator. Quickly he searches the marks on the control dial until he finds one marked "Nutwood", and then he turns the pointer until it is right opposite this mark. "Now," he says to Bill, "into the travel machine you go, and when I follow I'll slam the door and then we'll be on our way home." Pushing Bill forward he quickly follows, slams the door and, Whoosh! away they go.

The next thing they know is that they have landed in a large snow heap right in the middle of Mr. Bear's garden. "Good gracious!" says Mrs. Bear, "wherever have you come from?" "The South Sea Islands," chuckles Rupert; "but it's a long story so can Bill stay to tea, please, Mummie?" Mrs. Bear agrees, and Rupert hears Bill mutter to himself, "Well, thank goodness that is over, I'll never be inquisitive again as long as I live." Rupert grins. "Until the next time, Bill," he says as they go in to tea.

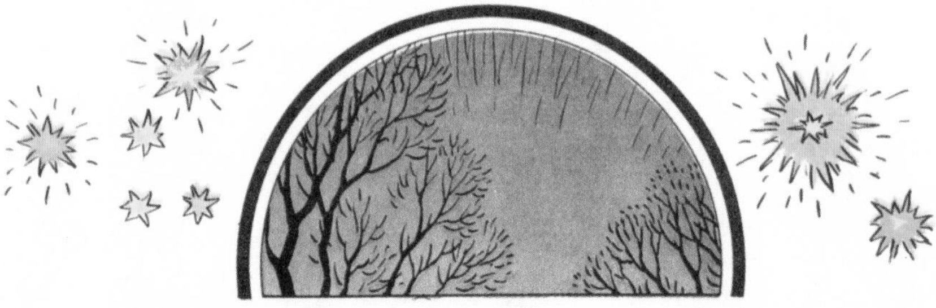

RUPERT and the BIG BANG

Rupert gets a scare, Nutwood a shaking and once again Bingo's plans go wrong.

Rupert and the Big Bang

RUPERT FOLLOWS BINGO

*Says Bill one day, "It isn't fair,
The master's praising Bingo there."*

*To their surprise, the master comes
And grumbles at the jealous chums.*

*He says, "You should help Bingo too,"
But Rupert wonders what to do.*

*So Rupert follows Bingo now,
To see if he can help, somehow.*

After school one day Rupert is chatting with his pals Bill Badger and Algy Pug. "I say, look over there," says Bill. "Why is the schoolmaster patting Bingo on the head like that?" As they watch, all three feel themselves getting jealous. Although they have spoken very quietly, the master turns and comes over to the little group. "I heard what you said and I'm surprised," he says solemnly. "Bingo is very clever and is learning science. Instead of being jealous I do wish you would help him."

Out in the road the little friends look at each other. "The master must have sharp ears," mutters Algy. "I didn't mean him to hear what I was saying." Just then Bingo the brainy pup passes them running the other way. Bill and Algy run off towards their homes, but Rupert keeps Bingo in sight. To his surprise the brainy pup goes down to the wall of an old deserted building. "This is very odd," says Rupert. "Why does he have to come to this queer place to do his new work?"

RUPERT OFFERS TO HELP

A smell of burning makes it plain,
That Bingo's hard at work again.

The puppy stays inside, and so
Poor Rupert sighs, "I think I'll go."

A little later on that day,
The puppy calls upon his way.

He wants some cord and paper too,
So Rupert sees what he can do.

Reaching the ruins Rupert can see no sign of Bingo. He drops his satchel and creeps down to the door and listens. There is no sound from Bingo, and he pauses. Then he sniffs. "There's an awful smell as if something is burning," he murmurs. "I wonder if science always smells like that." Rupert hesitates and then decides to put off helping Bingo until some other time. So he creeps away and runs to his own cottage. In the garden he finds his father sweeping up sticks and rubbish into a heap.

Rupert takes paper and matches and tries to start a fire, but the pile is too wet to catch alight. From nearby comes a voice. "Pssst, Rupert, are you busy? Can I come in?" Turning, he sees that Bingo is peering round the gate. "You're the person I want to see," cries Rupert. "The schoolmaster says that you are learning science. Can I help?" But Bingo won't tell him. "It's all rather secret," he says. "I've really come to ask you if you can find me some cardboard or thick paper."

RUPERT HEARS A BANG

Up in the lumber room they find,
Exactly what he has in mind.

Back now with Bingo Rupert goes,
Though what he's doing, goodness knows.

As off to school they go next day,
They hear a bang not far away.

It's late, and Bingo hasn't come,
What can have happened to their chum?

Rupert gets permission and takes Bingo to the little lumber room. Cardboard is soon found and Bingo gives a happy cry. "Is that a piece of spare wall-paper?" he cries. "It's exactly what I want for my work." They leave Mrs. Bear's cottage to go to the old ruins. "I knew you did your work here," says the little bear. "Can I come and see it?" To his disappointment Bingo shakes his head. "I'd rather you didn't," he says, "but I'll bring you something that will make your bonfire burn!"

Next morning Rupert joins up with Bill and Algy on the way to school. "Well," smiles Bill, "have you found out what science means yet?" Before he can say much more there is a distant bang and a little smoke appears above the trees. "Oh dear, Bingo's hide-out is over there," thinks Rupert anxiously. During morning school Rupert notices that one person is missing, and he gets more anxious than ever. "I say," he whispers, "does anyone know why Bingo isn't here?"

RUPERT GETS HIS FIRELIGHTERS

They meet him later, but again
The brainy pup will not explain.

Now Rupert is surprised to see,
That Bingo's hiding by a tree.

And then, to Rupert's great surprise,
"These squibs are yours!" the puppy cries.

Then Bingo sets a squib alight,
To show that they will work all right.

After school Bill and Algy stop at the village shop, when to Rupert's amazement, Bingo himself comes striding along with a parcel under his arm. "Hi, Bingo, come in here and buy some fireworks with us," cries Algy. But Bingo only gives a laugh. "No thanks, you can have them," he chuckles. Rupert, Bill and Algy all buy a few fireworks, and then the little bear sets out for home. Before he has gone very far a small figure pops up from behind a tree so suddenly that Rupert starts violently.

Bingo unpacks his parcel and produces three large squibs. "I promised you something to set fire to that pile of rubbish. These will do it," he says. Rupert stares. "My, what whoppers!" he cries. "Where did you get them?" Bingo once again looks mysterious. Rupert asks Bingo how he is to use the big squibs so the brainy pup sticks one of them in the trunk of a tree and sets light to it. "You see," says Bingo, "you must poke a squib into your pile of rubbish and it will dry and burn in no time."

RUPERT IS LOST IN THE DARKNESS

Their fireworks make a grand display,
When all the chums meet late that day.

The sky is filled now with a glow,
"What can it be?" they want to know.

The light goes out and down they fall,
For now they cannot see at all.

"Come on!" cries Rupert, "we must shout,
Or else we never shall get out."

Rupert takes the two remaining squibs that Bingo has given him and hides them carefully in his room. As soon as it is dark he joins his pals on the common and they have a fine time with the fireworks that they have bought in the shop. Suddenly Rupert stops. "Look over there!" he cries. "That glow in the sky. Someone has better fireworks than ours!" Soon all the pals see the big new light and, leaving their little fire, they go up the slope to get a better view.

While the bright light is in the sky the little pals have no difficulty in making their way towards it, but all at once it fades and goes right out, leaving them in pitch darkness. Next minute they are tumbling into a rough hollow that nobody has seen. They scramble up, moving slowly and cautiously along. Then Rupert stops. "This is no good," he declares. "We must call for help. Now, then, altogether, one, two, three . . . HELP!" They all strain their ears but there is only silence.

RUPERT GETS INTO TROUBLE

At last they hear somebody there,
Then find, with joy, it's Mr. Bear.

Thinks Rupert, "Daddy does look stern;
I'll try to make his bonfire burn."

He pokes the squib inside all right,
Then asks his father for a light.

The squib goes off with mighty sound,
And scatters all the pile around.

They call and call again and, to their joy, there is a distant answering shout. Mr. Bear appears carrying a lantern on a pole and soon guides the truants back to Nutwood but everyone is angry with them for causing so much anxiety. Next day, after school, Rupert wonders how he can make his father happy again. Then he thinks of Bingo's big squibs. "Look, Daddy," he says nervously, "I've got something here that should burn up that wet pile in the garden. May I go and do it for you?"

"I'm surprised that you have any large fireworks after your outing last night," says Mr. Bear. Rupert doesn't answer, but takes one of the squibs and, kneeling down, pushes it into the heart of the pile. When he has lit the pile Rupert gives the matches back to his father. The squib fizzes and splutters merrily and then without any warning, it explodes and with a terrific bang bits of wet pile are flung all over the garden again and Rupert and his father are sent staggering back with the shock.

RUPERT QUESTIONS BINGO

Now Mr. Bear is cross again,
And makes his little son explain.

As off to Bingo Rupert flies,
He sees a cloud of smoke arise.

He hurries on in great alarm,
Quite sure his chum has come to harm.

Now Bingo comes out looking gay,
And hears what Rupert has to say.

Mr. Bear bends down angrily and picks up the last of the squibs. "Tell me where you got these dreadful dangerous things from," he shouts. Seeing his father is annoyed, Rupert has to explain where the squibs came from. "Well," says Mr. Bear sternly, "tell Bingo that he has no business to have such things or give them away!" Rupert hurries away with the third squib. At length, Bingo's secret hide-out comes in sight, and as he watches, a cloud of smoke is shot up from the broken-down ruins!

He is thoroughly puzzled. "What on earth is Bingo up to?" he thinks. "I must find out the secret of all the bangs," he cries. "Hi, Bingo, are you there? Are you hurt?" To his relief he hears Bingo's voice from another part of the ruin. "I say, Bingo," gasps Rupert, "where did you get those squibs? One of them went wrong and blew up our rubbish heap and then I had to tell Daddy that it was yours." "Here, steady on!" cries Bingo. "Let's see that squib."

RUPERT SEES THAT FACTORY

But soon the smile fades from his face,
When Rupert tells what's taken place.

"Come in with me," the pup replies,
"And I will show you my surprise."

He points to fireworks on a shelf,
And says, "I made them all myself."

Now Bingo brings one, long and round,
He scarce can lift it from the ground.

Bingo gazes at the last of the squibs. "Good gracious!" he says. "The two I gave you must have been the wrong sort. This one would go off with a bang, too." "But tell me, where did you buy them?" insists Rupert. Bingo grins. "I didn't," he says, "I made them!" The little bear stares in amazement. Bingo thinks for a minute. "You already know part of my secret," he says, "I may as well tell you the rest. I've found out how to make gunpowder! Come on inside and I'll show you."

Leading the way into the inner room Bingo points out with pride all sorts of fireworks, arranged on the shelves. "Why, lots of them are covered with our old wall-paper!" cries Rupert. "I'd no idea that science meant making gunpowder!" Bingo looks doubtful. "I expect science means making other things, too," he says, "but gunpowder is enough to be going on with," and he turns down some steps to the cellar and with some puffing and grunting picks up a huge firework from the floor.

RUPERT GETS BURIED IN RUINS

"I'll help you," Rupert cries, and so
Out to the open field they go.

Says Bingo, "We must stand well back,
With powder I will lay a track."

"Oh dear!" owns Bingo to his chum,
"I'm nervous now the time has come."

Next moment, with a frightful din,
The walls and roof come tumbling in.

The two little friends carry the firework out of the cellar and into the open air. "Shall we set it off here, just by the door?" says Rupert. Bingo looks at it. "I'd feel happier if it was farther away," he murmurs. They slither and scramble up the loose stones away from the ruins. "Mind you don't drop your end," says Bingo nervously, as the young friends put the big firework down between two boulders. To Rupert's surprise Bingo carefully lays a trail of gunpowder away from the firework.

Bingo lays the trail of gunpowder right into the strongest room in the ruins. "We should be safe here whatever happens," says the brainy pup. He lights the end of the trail and they watch the sparks fizzing out of the door. Just as they think the trail must have failed there is a most shattering crash. The whole earth is shaken, the air is filled with dust, the ruins topple down and the entrance is blocked. Luckily for Rupert and Bingo a great beam prevents the ceiling from falling.

RUPERT TAKES A LETTER

The chums are shaking now with fright,
But otherwise they are all right.

They're rescued soon by Mr. Bear,
Who scolds the most unhappy pair.

When mother sees her dirty son,
She gasps, "Whatever have you done!"

And Mr. Bear next day sends word,
To tell the master what's occurred.

For the first few minutes after the big bang the two little pals stand in the darkness too frightened to move. After what seems hours the two friends hear someone working above, and soon there is a hole big enough for them to crawl through. They find Mr. Bear lifting another beam. He stares at them in complete astonishment. "That terrible bang shook every cottage in Nutwood. Whatever was it?" he says sternly. "Oh, please, I was only helping Bingo with his science," says the little bear anxiously.

Mrs. Bear is horrified to see them. "Good gracious! I've never seen you in such a mess," she cries. "Come and have a bath this minute." Next morning Rupert is given a letter to take to school and the master looks very grave when he reads it. "Dear, dear—tut-tut," he murmurs. "I would never have let Bingo learn science if I had known he was going to blow the place up. Anyway, you are not to blame. I'll attend to Bingo afterwards." And he leads the way to morning class.

RUPERT and the EMPTY COTTAGE

Here you can read Pong Ping's answer to the question, "Can there be smoke without a fire?"

RUPERT MAKES A BOW & ARROW

Says Rupert Bear, "These shoots will do,
To make a bow, and arrows too."

Just then, Pong-Ping comes round the bend,
He's talking to a Chinese friend.

So Rupert leaves the two alone,
And then meets Algy, on his own.

He wants to look like Robin Hood,
And play at outlaws in the wood.

Wandering by the edge of the forest Rupert sees some slender shoots and decides to cut one or two to make a bow and some arrows. When he has taken a long one and stripped it he looks for his pals. Hearing voices he enters the wood. There he sees Pong-Ping, the Peke, walking with a strange little man. Rupert hesitates. "That's the Chinese Mandarin," he murmurs. "They seem to be talking very earnestly. Perhaps I had better not interrupt them." And he trots away again.

Continuing his search for his friends Rupert discovers Algy Pug gazing cheerfully at something shapeless in his hands. "Look, Rupert," he cries, "I've found somebody's hat. Does it fit me?" He sticks a feather in the band and pops it on his head. "Do I look like Robin Hood?" he asks. "No, not very much," laughs Rupert, "you're too plump." Then he gets an idea. "But there's no harm in pretending," he adds. "Why shouldn't we pretend we're in Sherwood Forest?"

RUPERT INSPECTS THE COTTAGE

To start their game they gaily run,
Then Edward says he'll join the fun.

An empty cottage Rupert spies,
"Let's make that our H.Q.," he cries.

It's rather queer inside, and so
They search the cottage, high and low.

Up in the loft goes Rupert Bear,
To make quite sure it's empty there.

Algy thinks the idea is a grand one. "We shall want to find more of our pals first," he says. Before long they meet Edward Trunk and hurry to rope him in. "We're pretending we're a gang of outlaws, will you join us?" asks Rupert. Edward is very keen and asks what he shall do to start. "Well, first we want a secret headquarters," says Rupert, "and look, there is just the place." They run to a crumbling old cottage half hidden by bushes in the very depths of the wood.

The three pals rather timidly enter the old cottage. "This is a queer place," says Algy, "I don't like it very much." "It has a huge fireplace, but I can't see up the chimney," says Edward, "the flue bends before it reaches the top." Rupert gazes around and then climbs a rickety ladder to the dark loft where he finds nothing but a lot of dirt and a few bats. "The cottage is very empty," he declares, "but if we can clean it up a bit it should be all right for a band of outlaws."

RUPERT HEARS OF THE SMOKE

"All right," says Rupert, "now we'll start,
And each get ready for his part."

The outlaw band is ready quite,
With sword and stave and bow to fight.

Now Willie Mouse comes running by,
"Do stop and play with us," they cry.

"I've just come past that little house,
"The chimney's smoking!" says the Mouse.

After looking through the tiny building the three friends wander out of the wood. Algy has got over his uneasy feeling about the cottage. "People say that there's something odd in that place," he says, "but so long as we're all there together I don't mind a bit." "Then lets get ourselves prepared," says Rupert, "then we can pull in some more pals." Soon they are busy, Edward making a wooden sword, Algy cutting himself a strong staff, and Rupert finishing arrows and stringing his bow.

When the three pals have done their preparations they look for more friends and the first one they find is Willie the mouse. "Hi, Willie, come and join us in our game," cries Rupert. "We're pretending we're outlaws and our secret lair is that weird old cottage in the wood." Willie stares. "But you can't use that place," he says. "There's somebody there. I caught sight of it a few minutes ago and there was smoke coming out of the chimney!" The others stare in astonishment.

RUPERT SEES SMOKING CHIMNEY

They hardly let their chum explain,
Before they all rush back again.

And when the cottage comes in sight,
They find that Willie Mouse is right.

Now Rupert cannot make this out,
For there is still no one about.

"Stay there!" he whispers, "I will creep
Close to the wall, and take a peep."

Rupert can hardly believe what Willie has said. "Why we were there only a little time ago," he cries. "The place was in an awful mess. Nobody could have been there for ages. Surely you must have been mistaken." "The only thing to do is to go and look," says Edward. So they all make their way into the heart of the wood until they come in sight of the cottage. Then they stop and gaze in astonishment. "There, what did I tell you?" says Willie. "Wasn't I right about the smoke?"

Feeling very shaken at the sight of the smoke coming out of the chimney the four pals sidle around, keeping themselves under cover until they are in a bush near the cottage. Peering through it they keep watch. "This is weird," whispers Rupert, "the place is as quiet as ever. Nobody going in or out and there are no voices, but *something* must be causing that smoke." Determined to solve the mystery, he leaves his bow and arrows and creeps gingerly towards the window.

RUPERT FINDS SMOKE WITHOUT FIRE

But when he looks around the door,
The room is empty as before.

There is no fire that they can see,
It's very odd, they all agree.

That smoke so mystifies the chums,
They have to know from whence it comes.

The bushes are so thick and tall,
They can't get to the back at all.

After cautiously listening for any sound Rupert reaches the door and peeps inside the little room. Then he gives a gasp. "Hi, come in here, you chaps," he cries. "This is the oddest thing ever. The cottage is as empty as it was before!" He runs to the fireplace and gazes upwards but finds, as Edward Trunk had done earlier, that the flue bends and he cannot see up the chimney. "There hasn't been a fire here for ages," he says, as the others run to join him.

The smoke from the chimney completely puzzles the pals. Willie doesn't like it and runs away. "I wish we knew more about this cottage," says Rupert. "There's no way out of that room except the door and the chimney." "Let's have a look at the back of the cottage," says Edward. But the trees and bushes have been allowed to grow so thickly close to the walls that even Edward cannot butt his way through. "Perhaps we can find a way round farther from the cottage," says Rupert.

RUPERT CONSULTS TIGERLILY

Now Rupert thinks that they should go,
To find somebody who will know.

The Conjurer he thinks he'll try,
But meets his daughter just nearby.

Young Tigerlily is most keen
To find out what the chums have seen.

But when she sees the hearth quite bare,
She cries, "It's magic, I declare!"

The three friends try to work round towards the back of the cottage until they are tired. The bushes of that part of the wood are so old and thick that they can force no way through, and all the time the smoke steadily pours out. "I know," suggests Rupert, "let's go and find some of the clever people of the village and ask if they can explain the mystery." The others agree and they separate. Rupert thinks of the Conjurer and near his house he meets Tigerlily picking flowers.

Rapidly explaining what he is worried about, Rupert quickly interests the Conjurer's daughter and she hurries him back to the old cottage and then inside, where she looks steadily at the hearth-stone before peeping up the chimney just as Rupert and Edward had done. "This too great mystery for me," murmurs Tigerlily. "My Daddy can make smoke by burning many strange things, but even he cannot make smoke without fire. This very dark magic.

RUPERT THINKS OF PONG-PING

Now Rupert ponders once again,
There must be someone can explain!

Old William is the next to come,
He shakes his head and looks quite glum.

The old man says, "I'll not go near;
It is the pixies there I fear."

"I know," says Rupert, "I will bring,
Our clever little friend, Pong-Ping."

When Tigerlily can give no explanation the mystery gets deeper. "Who can I ask next?" murmurs Rupert. At that moment Algy and Edward appear. They have found old William and the ancient man is hobbling along between them. The young people talk excitedly and manage to make him understand what they want and then they show him the chimney smoking. To their disappointment he will not go into the cottage. " 'Tis a pesky place," he mutters into his beard

Old William turns to the expectant little group. "Yon cottage hasn't been lived in for many a year," he grunts hoarsely. "Most folks won't go nigh it. They do say the pixies live there, and I don't doubt that explains any queer thing like that smoke." The young people look baffled, but Rupert isn't satisfied. "There must be a more likely explanation than that," he thinks. Suddenly he has an idea and, taking to his heels, he runs to find Pong-Ping.

RUPERT TELLS HIS STORY

When Pong-Ping hears about the smoke,
He simply treats it as a joke.

He says, "I'm glad you came to me;
I can explain it all, you see."

As Rupert is so keen to know,
To solve the mystery they go.

A tunnel leads them to a room,
That might be passed by in the gloom.

Rupert tells Pong-Ping everything that has happened that day. "Your old Mandarin friend must be very wise," he says. "I wish you'd bring him to explain that queer smoke." To his amazement the little Peke only bursts out laughing. "You were too polite this morning, Rupert," he chuckles. "If you had come and spoken to us when you saw me walking with the Mandarin you would have solved everything by now. Come and let me show you."

Pong-Ping leads the way by a long winding route until he enters a narrow track that tunnels through thick tangled bushes getting more dark and gloomy until it ends abruptly in a dark doorway. "Whatever's this?" quavers Rupert. "Don't you recognize it?" asks the little Peke in a humorous voice. "It's the basement of your mysterious cottage. This is the only way in. It has a fireplace too, and the flue bends up to the same chimney that serves the other one."

RUPERT MEETS A PET DRAGON

Says Pong-Ping to the little bear,
"Go to the wood and watch from there."

A cloud of smoke appears once more,
Much larger than the one before.

Now Rupert has a dreadful fright,
A dragon's head pops into sight.

"Don't run!" says Pong-Ping, "I'll explain,
I have the dragon on a chain."

Rupert is still mystified. "D'you mean that you've been causing the smoke by having a fire down there?" he asks. Pong-Ping grins and waves him back. "You'd better not come into the basement," he says. "Go back into the wood and wait for me. Then you'll understand everything." So, in great bewilderment, Rupert retreats down the dark path until he is in the open. All at once he starts violently. Another cloud of smoke has appeared through the bushes.

As he gazes, Rupert gets the shock of his life, for the great head of a dragon pokes through the leaves and gently breathes smoke at him. He turns to run but next instant Pong-Ping appears, still smiling and leading the creature by a chain. "You see?" laughs the Peke. "My friend the Mandarin has business here, and he brought with him his old pet dragon which he asked me to take care of." "B-but why put him in the basement?" gasps Rupert.

RUPERT EXPLAINS TO HIS PALS

"He breathes much fire," goes on the Peke,
"But really he is kind and meek."

"Well," Rupert laughs, "I'm very glad,
To know the dragon isn't bad."

"Good-bye," he calls, then off he goes,
To tell the others all he knows.

Now that the mystery is past,
They can begin their game at last.

Pong-Ping smiles again. "I have a little pet Dragon of my own and they might have quarrelled," he says. "The old one breathes a lot of smoke and sometimes a lot of fire, so I made a comfy bed for him in that basement and made him breath all his smoke into the fireplace. So that he couldn't set light to anything. That was the smoke you saw. Now I'm going to take him for a short walk. Good-bye." And breathing a sigh of relief Rupert scampers back to his pals.

The little bear finds the others very puzzled because the chimney has stopped smoking and he quickly explains everything. Old William grunts. "I still believe it was the pixies. I don't hold with dragons and such," he says, as he hobbles away. But Tigerlily is pleased and runs away to tell her daddy all about it. Then Rupert takes his pals and picks up his bow and arrows. "Now at last we can get on with our game of being a band of outlaws!" he laughs.

RUPERT'S GARDEN PUZZLE

The old Professor has invited Rupert and Bill Badger to see his new garden. When they arrive they find that he has laid out his paths in a very curious way.

"Come along," calls the Professor. "I'll give a bar of chocolate to the first one of you to reach me. You mustn't cross the grass anywhere, and don't walk over any of the white lines."

"What fun!" laughs Rupert. "Let's try. I'll enter on the right and you go to the left." "Right-ho" says Bill.

Which of them wins the bar of chocolate?

FOLLOW
RUPERT
EVERY
MORNING
IN THE
DAILY EXPRESS

NOTICE
SOLUTION TO PUZZLE, page 2
Run the Engine forward to B, back it up the left hand line, push the orange truck into the siding at A and leave it there. Return to B, then to C and push the blue truck up to the orange one. Couple them both together and pull them to C. Push them on to the curve towards B. Drop the orange truck, return to C with the blue one, push it to A and leave it. You can now pull the orange truck to C and push it on to the right hand line. Finally go round and fetch the blue one on to the left

Made & Printed Photo-offset
by Greycaines, Watford & London.